UNIVERSITY OF LEEDS

—

LIBRARY PUBLICATIONS
No. 3

LIBRARY PUBLICATIONS

1. OFFOR (R.)   A descriptive guide to the Libraries of the University of Leeds, 1947

1a.   —   —— Supplement, 1949.

2. WHITAKER (H.) The Harold Whitaker collection of county atlases, road-books and maps presented to the University of Leeds. A catalogue by Harold Whitaker, 1947.

3.   A Catalogue of the Gosse Correspondence in the Brotherton Collection consisting mainly of letters written to Sir Edmund Gosse in the period from 1867 to 1928, 1950.

Edmund Gosse

A CATALOGUE OF THE GOSSE CORRESPONDENCE IN THE BROTHERTON COLLECTION

CONSISTING MAINLY OF LETTERS
WRITTEN TO SIR EDMUND GOSSE
IN THE PERIOD FROM 1867 TO 1928

with an Introduction by PHILIP GOSSE

THE BROTHERTON LIBRARY, LEEDS
1950

PREFACE

Edmund Gosse, the son and father of men of letters, was himself, though for two periods of his life more or less nominally a librarian, and always a book-collector, in essence an industrious and more than competent essayist, critic and historian of literature. Of the literature, indeed, which is secondary to pure creation (rarely essayed by him), he became in his later years a recognized doyen. And, whether because of his early experience in the British Museum's Department of Printed Books, or because in that earlier youth, so wonderfully described by him in *Father and Son*, he had helped his father, a marine biologist of distinction, to range and record specimens, or merely because of a life of journalism, he developed methodical habits to a rare degree. No article of his was ever over or under the prescribed tale of words, or "turned in" late by even an hour. He was, in fact, the Editor's dream-contributor, and had the race of printers' devils still existed in his day, they would, so far as he was concerned, have found their occupation gone. (When did they disappear? Was it when the telephone, that chartered interrupter of literary labours, came in?)

An aspect of the intense tidiness of Gosse's mind and habits is to be seen in his correspondence. He must have preserved it nearly entire, large as it was and covering a long period and a wide range of friends and acquaintances, foreign as well as English, representing the chief literary movements in England, France, Scandinavia, and other lands.

Such a collection is obviously a quarry for students of literature; and after Gosse's death, which happened in 1928, Lord Brotherton, who had turned his attention to the manuscripts and correspondence of leading contemporaries, was naturally glad to be allowed to purchase the collection from the writer's representatives; it was his largest and much his most important acquisition in this kind. And when, in 1935, his executors, in accordance with his known wishes, presented his whole Library to the University of Leeds, to which he had given the great Library building named after him, the Gosse Correspondence came with it, to be a notable possession of the Brotherton Collection.

So notable is it, that, increasingly during the past fifteen years, enquiries relating to it are received from students, and, as time goes on, more will certainly come. The Brotherton Collection Committee therefore decided to publish a catalogue of it, in order at least to let those concerned know with whom Gosse corresponded, with indication of the number of letters to or from each and the dates. This is doubtless but a bare skeleton; yet it is difficult to see what else could be produced at this stage, short of a selection of the letters themselves, which would involve great labour, great expense and great delay, during which last the essential facts would continue to be kept from those needing to know them, and valuable study of the correspondence thus effectually discouraged. Moreover 1949 was the centenary of Gosse's birth, and though the exact year has passed, 1950 is not too far from it for a publication intended to do him honour.

The Committee have been fortunate in that their project has had hearty encouragement from Gosse's son, Dr. Philip Gosse, who has further earned their gratitude by contributing the Introduction which follows.

The Committee's thanks are also due to the following for permission to reproduce letters in facsimile:—Viscount Scarsdale, for Lord Curzon's letter; Mr. Laurence Housman, for A. E. Housman's letter; Mr. William James and Messrs. Paul R. Reynolds & Son, for Henry James's letter; and Mrs. Louise Powell, for Walter Sickert's letter.

The Catalogue is the work of Mr. A. Whitworth, formerly Sub-Librarian in charge of the Brotherton Collection; Mr. D. Cox, the present Sub-Librarian; Miss M. A. Hamilton and Mr. H. G. Tupper, Assistant Librarians; with some help from other members of the Staff of the Brotherton Library; the whole having been overseen by Mr. B. S. Page, University Librarian and Keeper of the Brotherton Collection.

For the Brotherton Collection Committee:

ARUNDELL ESDAILE,

Chairman.

22nd May, 1950

INTRODUCTION

My father held pronounced views on certain subjects; one of these was punctuality. He himself was never late; in fact, he was liable to arrive at some dinner-party so very early as to embarrass both his hosts and my mother. And if he was always punctual himself, he expected punctuality of his friends. Woe betide a guest who arrived more than a few minutes late for a social gathering at home !

This possibly is the reason why I remember so very few occasions in my childhood on which any guest arrived late at a party at our house. I don't know if Henry James was by nature punctual, or whether he achieved that admirable quality as the result of my father's training; but I do remember how at the stroke of nine by the clock in the drawing-room any Monday evening, we would hear the front-door bell ring, and after a short spell of muffled conversation in the hall, Mr. Henry James—in those days wearing a beard—would be ushered in by the parlour-maid.

And this punctuality applied also to his correspondence. Every letter he received was immediately replied to. The moment breakfast was finished he would gather up his morning's post, bound upstairs two or three steps at a time to his study, and at once get down to the task of replying to each letter. And not only did he reply at once, but he expected, and did not hesitate to demand an early answer to those letters he wrote to his friends.

Occasionally this habit led to unfortunate results; for he was, it must be confessed, quick to take offence, often where none was intended, and he would dash off some pungent or stinging reply which was apt to lead to a—generally temporary—estrangement with some friend. Some such fiery epistle he would send to be posted forthwith by the parlour-maid.

My mother, who most thoroughly understood her husband, when she suspected that the urgent letter would not have been written except in the heat of the moment, would often quietly slip out of the room and take back the suspect letter from the maid. Next morning, when probably my father had cooled off and was beginning a little to regret his hasty wrath, she would hand the letter to him and explain that by some oversight it had not been posted. By such tactful subterfuge many a friendship, often of years' standing, was preserved. For my father maintained, and never tired of impressing it on us, that friendship was a precious thing, and that once a friendship was made it should not be left to look after itself, but, like some delicate plant, should be tended and nourished to preserve it.

The best way to do this was, in his opinion, to write letters from time to time to absent friends and so keep alive the glowing embers which otherwise tended to cool and become extinguished. This pleasant habit, one rare in the case of such a busy man, of keeping in touch with old friends and not waiting for some particular occasion or excuse to do so, accounts for the large number of his friendships, which continued for many years—in many cases until the death of one or other of the correspondents.

Another of my father's idiosyncrasies was his jackdaw-like amassing of any letter or document which in his opinion might be, or might possibly become, of future interest to others. This foible or weakness for keeping old letters, added to his habit of writing letters and expecting his friends to write back to him, accounts for the enormous mass of correspondence which he left behind him when he died, and which threatened to become an embarrassment to his literary executor.

But owing to the generosity of the late Lord Brotherton most of these letters are now in the safe keeping of the Leeds University Library and are there for the inspection and use of present and future students of English literature and of English literary life during the latter part of the nineteenth and the early part of the twentieth century.

Recently there have been added to the collection some sixty little pocket diaries in which my father noted down every dinner-party, every lecture or committee meeting or other appointment. These books include the name of almost everyone well or less well known in English letters during his life-time, as well as a meticulous record of the articles he wrote for various magazines and periodicals, with the sums he was paid for them; these and the royalties he received for his books are all carefully noted down.

One great source of friendship which no doubt stimulated the writing of letters was my parents' habit of giving Sunday afternoon parties. When my parents married in 1875 and until they found a house of their own, they were guests of their brother-in-law Lawrence Alma Tadema, the painter. If my father was the soul of hospitality, the Alma Tademas ran him very close later on with their famous Tuesday evenings at Grove End Road, which were as popular with painters, sculptors and musicians as my father and mother's Sunday afternoon and supper parties were to become with writers and men and women of letters in general.

On the very day he was appointed translator to the Board of Trade, with the princely salary of four hundred pounds a year, the date of his marriage was fixed, and as soon as ever the young couple were able to, they took up their residence at 29 Delamere Terrace in a somewhat dingy row of houses facing the Paddington canal. Here the parties which were to continue for so many years began, and for the next fifty years and more my father wrote down the name of every guest, famous or otherwise, in the *Book of Gosse*. It still exists, a long narrow volume, measuring thirty-two by four inches, bound in faded parchment, containing 354 pages, and now in the Cambridge University Library. On every page is written down in his beautiful handwriting, under the date, the name of every guest who came to tea, and the names of those who stayed on for supper are under-lined.

No attempt has been made to give a mere list of all, or indeed many, of the names which occur, but I have tried to indicate when new names first appeared, and those which continued, often for many years.

The very first party of all took place on Sunday, 17th November, 1875. The guests on this auspicious occasion were Mr. and Mrs. William Rossetti, Mr. Colnaghi, Mrs. Lynn Linton, then at the height of her success with the publication of her popular novel *Patricia Kemball*, Mr. Herkomer, the painter, Mr. Austin Dobson, my father's fellow civil servant at the Board of Trade, and the Hon. J. Leicester Warren, later Lord de Tabley. On 10th June 1877, amongst the guests were Mr. and Mrs. Waterhouse, the Alma Tademas, and the poet O'Shaughnessy, as well as "ATOSSA (first appearance)", a much spoiled Persian cat which was destined to play an important part in the Gosse household.

My father describes somewhere a strange occurrence at

the British Museum when one day in 1873 he went for a chat with O'Shaughnessy. He found him with his head resting upon his arms, which were folded upon the table. "He raised his face to me," Gosse wrote, "in tears, and when I enquired what was the matter he replied by a question: 'Have you not seen the paper? Lord Lytton is dead,' When I hinted my surprise at his emotion he added: 'No one will ever know what he was to me'." My father enquired no further.

The name of Swinburne first appears in 1878, when he may have been brought by his old friend Walter Pater. From now onwards new names keep cropping up: Andrew Lang, George Saintsbury, Alfred Waterhouse the architect, and Walter Pollock. Next came Mr. and Mrs. Humphry Ward with Professor Fleming Jenkin, the engineer, followed on 10th July, 1880, by a near neighbour, Robert Browning. It was on a July evening a year later that Swinburne stayed on after tea to supper (indicated in the *Book* by the under-lining of his name), the other guest being "Mr. Watts," who years afterwards as Theodore Watts-Dunton was to act as the poet's companion or, as some unkind persons asserted, his jailer, at "The Pines."

During this early period it is notable what a large number of names occur of well-known artists, painters and sculptors, though in later years the artists fell away and the writers largely took their place: artists such as Alfred Parsons, Frank Dicksee, Frank Millet, Luke Fildes, Alma Tadema, John Sargent, Joseph Pennell, Fred Barnard of *Punch*, Edwin Abbey and Marcus Stone, while sculpture is represented by Thomas Brock, Alfred Gilbert, Onslow Ford and Hamo Thornycroft. The reason why my parents knew so many artists is explained by the fact that, when they married, my mother, then Miss Nelly Epps, was studying painting in Ford Madox Brown's studio together with the painter's daughter. At gatherings at his studio in Fitzroy Square the young critic met the main body of the pre-Raphaelites, William Morris, Holman Hunt, the Rossettis, Swinburne and Burne-Jones, with Whistler, O'Shaughnessy, Theo Marzials, Francis Hueffer, Val Prinsep and many others of the disciples. It was at one of these gatherings in 1870 that my father first met his future bride.

One name which was destined to be entered in the *Book*

of Gosse for many years to come first appears under the date 3rd December, 1887—" Mr. Henry James," while further down the list is yet another old-friend-to-be, " Mr. Thomas Hardy." Another gathering of writers who were to become well-known took place one afternoon when in the list of guests we find, besides Hardy and James, Andrew Lang, Rider Haggard, Walter Pater and Robert Bridges.

It was a disappointment to the writer of these notes that he was unable to find any record of a visit by Robert Louis Stevenson, for he can just remember as a very small boy gazing at a figure seated on the balcony of our house over-looking the Regent's canal and draped in a bright red silk shawl lent him by his hostess. The reason for this absence of the name of one of my father's dearest friends is, I think, that owing to his bad health R.L.S. never attended one of our crowded parties, but preferred to come alone; and as only Sunday guests are included in the *Book* his name is missing. Years afterwards his widow came to tea accompanied by Lloyd Osbourne.

In 1887 a new set of names begins, of young men who used to attend my father's Clark lectures at Cambridge: Walter Raleigh, Harry Wilson, A. B. Cane, Rathbone, young Austen Chamberlain and others. By this time the artists were giving way to the writers—Mrs. Hodgson Burnett of *Little Lord Fauntleroy* fame, Arthur Waugh (my father's cousin and father of Alec and Evelyn Waugh), Henry Harland, editor of *The Yellow Book,* Oswald Crawfurd the novelist, and Walter Besant.

One day in 1891 a Miss Carrie Balestier, a young American lady, paid her first call, and a month later she called again with Mr. Rudyard Kipling, whose wife she was shortly to become. On the same afternoon we find Arthur Symons, followed shortly afterwards by Ernest Rhys and Hall Caine, whom I have to confess my father never ceased to make fun of. It is for a January evening a year later that we find the entry " Mr. and Mrs. Rudyard Kipling (recited B. R. Ballads)." Fresh names keep appearing: Robert Ross, who was to become a life-long friend; the poets William Watson and Richard Le Gallienne; Arthur Pinero the playwright; Owen Seaman, later editor of *Punch;* the novelist Gilbert Parker; Arthur Benson, then a master at Eton; Aubrey Beardsley, who was then art editor of *The Yellow Book,* before

joining Arthur Symons in the production of *The Savoy;*
and Anthony Hope Hawkins, who had just published
The Prisoner of Zenda, which met with such phenomenal
success that he felt justified in giving up the law to become
a professional writer. Kenneth Grahame of *The Golden Age,*
a cousin of Anthony Hope, was also a fairly regular visitor
to Delamere Terrace in the 1890's.

Although by now men of letters predominated, there were
also guests of other callings, as General Redvers Buller, soon to
become well known in the Boer War; Clifford Allbutt, recently appointed Regius Professor of Physic at Cambridge, and
Professor Ray Lankester, a fellow member of the Savile Club.

It must have been a remarkable party which is recorded
as taking place on 28th June, 1896. For one thing, there
were no fewer than eighty-five guests to tea that afternoon,
a notable achievement on my mother's part, for it was in
the old house by the canal, with only one maid to help.

Two events came back to my memory on reading this list
of names made out more than fifty years ago, both oddly
enough happening on the same afternoon. One is the
appearance of an unknown guest, Prince Karageorgevitch
of Servia. I remember him well, a tall black-bearded
romantic figure who might have just stepped out of one of
Anthony Hope's novels. As the drawing room door opened
and there was a sudden lull in the general conversation, the
little maid announced the newcomer as " Mr. George."
After the last of the guests had left, on my father remon-
strating with her, she explained that when she asked the
gentleman his name, he replied " Prince George," but she
knew that was not right, for she had often seen pictures of
Prince George in the newspapers.

The other incident which I well remember may be worth
while recording. Amongst our guests that afternoon was
Andrew Lang, tall, very handsome, with his dark eyes and
complexion and waving light grey hair. Also he was
behaving in what my father described as a tiresome way.
Lang was rather like a spoiled child, and although he could
be charming and polite when he wished, was apt to sulk for
no apparent reason. This was evidently one of his tiresome
days, for although my father had introduced various friends
to him, he stood aloof and alone, with his hands in his
pockets, leaning against a bookcase. His host, who believed

in keeping his guests in circulation, then brought up to Lang
a young man, about twenty-four years of age, small, dapper,
with smooth hair and somewhat drooping eyelids, and
immaculately dressed in the very height of the then pre-
vailing fashion, and in his clear stentorian voice begged to
introduce a young friend of his, who was most anxious to
meet him—" Mr. Max Beerbohm." The modest Max
evidently tried his best to get Lang to talk, but with little
success. Then a week or two later there appeared in one of
the illustrated monthlies a superb cartoon of Andrew Lang
apathetically lolling against a bookcase, signed with the
signature which was to become so famous—" Max."

As we turn the pages over we come across a constant
stream of new names, Mrs. Asquith and her stepson Raymond,
Mr. (now Sir) Edward Marsh, Arthur Balfour, Mrs. Pearl
Mary Teresa Craigie, known to novel-readers and theatre-
goers as John Oliver Hobbes.

Edmund Gosse was ever a sympathetic friend to and
encourager of young poets. One young man, aged twenty-
three, makes his first appearance on a Sunday in May 1909.
This is no other than Mr. Siegfried Sassoon, who met on
that occasion A. E. Housman, Lady Mary Kidd and E. F.
Benson. More young poets were to follow before long,
but in the meanwhile two more artists present themselves,
George Frampton and Walter Sickert, while literature is
represented by Laurence Binyon, André Gide, Mr. Percy
Lubbock and Hugh Walpole.

Now the young poets begin to come thick and fast: Mr.
Alfred Noyes, who had become a neighbour of ours at our
new and more spacious house in Hanover Terrace, Regent's
Park; Rupert Brooke; and an exotic and lovely Indian girl
poet, Sarojini Chattopadhyaya, later to become famous not
only as a poet but also for her political activities in India, as
Madam Sarojini Naidu. This dainty fawnlike creature, with
her large gazelle eyes, was then an undergraduate at, of all
places, Girton College, Cambridge, and never can any
student at that famous seat of learning have been more out
of her element. It was winter, and a Cambridge winter at
its worst, and the poor girl, fresh from balmy Hyderabad,
felt the cold intensely. I remember how delighted we all
were when she assured us that her doctor had ordered her
to wear flannel under her skin.

It was about this time that Lord and Lady Charnwood first came, and they continued life-long friends.

But to return to our poets. John Drinkwater is the next on the list, and on his first visit met the Belgian poet Emile Verhaeren, Mr. Max Beerbohm, Sir George Otto Trevelyan, and Mr. Compton Mackenzie.

We have now reached the autumn of 1917—we started forty-two years before—and it was on the 18th of November that Miss Edith Sitwell and her brother Lieutenant Sacheverell Sitwell (probably on leave from the trenches) first entered the door of 17 Hanover Terrace. True to family tradition the Sitwells preferred to come together—seldom singly—and in the following March the two came again accompanied this time by Captain Osbert Sitwell. The famous trio were henceforward to be constant and ever welcome visitors. Two other young poets who were often seen were J. C. Squire and Robert Nichols, with Logan Pearsall Smith, Lytton Strachey, Philip Guedalla, Robert and Sylvia Lynd, Powys Evans, Mr. Desmond MacCarthy, Montague Summers, Sir George Arthur and, most constant guest to supper of them all, George Moore.

But to continue this enumeration would be to run the risk of inflicting on the reader a mere tedious list of names. However, just one very last entry, but a unique one. On 29th August, 1920, when all London would or ought to have been "out of town," though apparently the Gosses were not, we read this entry: "Two ladies of Puerto Rico." Just that and nothing more. No other guests, no explanation of what brought them or what happened. Did the two señoritas speak nothing but Spanish? It is all very tantalizing.

It is to be hoped that these extracts from the *Book of Gosse* may help to explain why Edmund and Nelly Gosse had such a large circle of friends and why to-day the Brotherton Library possesses such a quantity of letters written to them by their friends.

It was a happy thought on the part of the Leeds University Library to choose this year, the centenary of his birth, to print this catalogue of letters, and no monument to the memory of Edmund Gosse could take a more suitable form, for friendship was indeed the very essence of his life.

PHILIP GOSSE.

December 1949.

PLATES

Facsimiles of letters to Sir Edmund Gosse from the Marquis Curzon of Kedleston, A. E. Housman, Henry James and Walter Sickert will be found between pages 24 and 25.

NOTE

Each entry in the catalogue contains:

(1)   The name of the writer of the letter or letters;

(2)   The name of the person to whom the letters are addressed, in those cases only (comparatively few) in which that person is other than Sir Edmund Gosse;

(3)   The number of letters (the numeral being in italics);

(4)   The date, or inclusive dates (dates in round brackets having been supplied from postmarks, those in square brackets being conjectural or having been added to the letters in another hand; the term "undated" is reserved for those letters about whose date no safe deduction seemed to be possible, and where a number of undated letters is specified, this number is to be taken as included in the total number indicated by the italicised numeral mentioned above).

For example, the entry—

FISHER (Herbert Albert Laurens). *21.* February 23, 1904—November 5, 1927; 1 undated—

indicates 21 letters from Mr. Fisher to Sir Edmund Gosse of which 1 is undated and the remainder cover the period mentioned.

Any other information given will, it is hoped, be self-explanatory. Cross-references, though somewhat fewer than full cataloguing practice would require, should be sufficient to prevent confusion.

Enquiries about the Gosse Correspondence should be addressed to: The University Librarian and Keeper of the Brotherton Collection, The Brotherton Library, The University, Leeds 2.

THE GOSSE CORRESPONDENCE

A

ABBEY (Edwin Austin). *8.* March 17, [1883]—October 29, [1885]; 1 undated.

ABERCROMBIE (Lascelles). *8.* [October 16 ?], (1914)—May 17, [1919]; 2 undated.

ABERDEEN AND TEMAIR (John Campbell Gordon, *1st Marquis of*), *see* GORDON (John Campbell), *1st Marquis of Aberdeen and Temair.*

ACHESON (Archibald Brabazon Sparrow), *4th Earl of Gosford. 1.* May 29, 1906.

ACTON (John Emerich Edward Dalberg), *1st Baron Acton of Aldenham. 1.* February 5, [1896].

ADAMS (William Henry Davenport). *1.* Undated.

AINGER (Alfred). *1.* January 18, 1898.

AIRLIE (Henrietta Blanche Ogilvy, *Countess of*), *see* OGILVY (Henrietta Blanche), *Countess of Airlie.*

AITCHISON (George). *2.* March 3, 1884; July 29, 1885.

AITKEN (George Atherton). *1.* May 17, 1907.

ALDEN (Henry Mills) [*for* Harper & Brothers, *publishers, New York*]. *3.* December 2, 1903—April 10, 1911.

ALDRICH (T. J.). *2.* November 23, 1919; June 13, 1920.

ALDRICH (Thomas Bailey). *3.* July 26, 1882—May 23, 1885.

ALEXANDER (Eleanor Jane). *1.* March 3, 1912.

ALEXANDER (*Sir* George). *1.* December 20, 1914.

ALI (Abdullah Yusuf), *see* YŪSUF 'ALĪ ('Abd Allāh).

ALI (Mehmed). *1.* March 20, 1928.

ALLBUTT (*Sir* Thomas Clifford). *1.* January 1, 1925.

ALLEN (Charles Grant Blairfindie). *2.* February 3, [1887]; October 25, [1894].

ALLEN (Phoebe) *to* BRIGHTWEN (Eliza). *3.* June 27, 1903—July 13, [1903].

ALLINGHAM (Helen) [Mrs. William Allingham]. *1.* April 29, 1915.

ALLINGHAM (William). *2.* April 26, 1872; June 15, 1874.

ALVERSTONE (Richard Everard Webster, *1st Viscount*), *see* WEBSTER (Richard Everard), *1st Viscount Alverstone of Alverstone.*

AMES (Percy Willoughby) [*for* the Royal Society of Literature of the United Kingdom]. *2.* May, 1910; July 2, 1910.

B

ANCASTER (Gilbert Heathcote-Drummond-Willoughby, *2nd Earl of*), *see* HEATHCOTE-DRUMMOND-WILLOUGHBY (Gilbert), *2nd Earl of Ancaster.*

ANDERSEN (Hans Christian). *4.* December 8, 1872—May 20, 1874.

—— *to* FOG (Brunn Juul), *Bishop, first, of Aarhus; afterwards, of Sjælland. 1.* May 13, 1874.

ANDERSON (Mary). *2.* Undated.

ANNALY (Lavinia Emily White, *Baroness*), *see* SPENCER (*Lady* Lavinia Emily), *afterwards* Baroness Annaly.

ANNALY (Luke Henry White, *4th Baron*), *see* WHITE (Luke Henry), *4th Baron Annaly of Annaly and Rathcline.*

ANSTEY (F.) *pseud.* [*i.e.* Thomas Anstey Guthrie], *see* GUTHRIE (Thomas Anstey), *pseud.* F. Anstey.

ANTRIM (William Randall McDonnell, *6th Earl of*), *see* McDONNELL (William Randall), *6th Earl of Antrim.*

APPELL (Paul Émile). *1.* April 1, 1925.

APPLETON (Charles Edward Cutts Birch). *1.* July 10, 1878.

ARCHER (William). *6.* March 22, 1898—June 16, 1908.

—— *from* BRADLEY (Andrew Cecil). *2.* Undated.

ARMOUR (George Allison). *2.* [October? 1884]; June 4, 1885.

ARMSTEAD (Henry Hugh). *13.* June 14, 1880—November 21, 1897.

ARNOLD (Matthew). *5.* June 24, [1882]—December 30, 1885.
Letter dated June 15, 1884: this is a transcript of the original, in Sir Edmund Gosse's hand.

ARRAN (Arthur Jocelyn Charles Gore, *6th Earl of*), *see* GORE (Arthur Jocelyn Charles), *6th Earl of Arran.*

ASBJÖRNSEN (Peter Christen). *9.* November 17, 1872—September 20, 1875.

—— *and others. 1* telegram. August 13, 1875.

ASHE (Thomas). *1.* April 24, 1876.

ASHTON (Arthur Jacob). *1.* August 9, 1901.

ASQUITH (Elizabeth Charlotte Lucy), *afterwards* Princess Bibesco, *see* BIBESCO (Elizabeth Charlotte Lucy), *Princess, neé* Asquith.

ASQUITH (Emma Alice Margaret), *Countess of Oxford and Asquith. 23.* May 6, (1911)—November 22, 1920; 3 undated. *Also 4* telegrams. July 10, 1920—November 4, 1920.

——*from* MILNES (Robert Offley Ashburton Crewe-), *1st Marquis of Crewe*. *1*. July 21, 1920.

ASQUITH (Helen Violet), *afterwards* Lady Helen Violet Bonham-Carter. *1*. June 4, 1913.

ASQUITH (Herbert Henry), *1st Earl of Oxford and Asquith*. *21*. July 24, 1903—March 5, 1925.
Letter dated December 4, 1914: enclosed is a letter from Viscount Simon to the Earl of Oxford, dated December 3, 1914.

—— *from* SIMON (John Allsebrook), *1st Viscount Simon of Stackpole Elidor*. *1*. December 3, 1914.
Enclosed in a letter from the Earl of Oxford to Sir Edmund Gosse, dated December 4, 1914.

ASTON (William George). *1*. September 30, 1895.

ATHOLL (John George Stewart-Murray, *8th Duke of*), *see* MURRAY (John George Stewart-), *8th Duke of Atholl*.

ATLAY (James), *Bishop of Hereford*. *1*. December 1, 1883.

AUBRY (Georges Jean). *2*. August 17, 1917; November 30, 1917.

AUSTIN (Alfred) *to* LANE (John). *1*. December 2, 1909.

AUTOMOBILE-CLUB DE FRANCE. *1*. September 20, 1916.

AVEBURY (John Lubbock, *1st Baron*), *see* LUBBOCK (John), *1st Baron Avebury of Avebury*.

AVERY (Edward). *1*. May 20, 1884.

B

BAILEY (Joseph Henry Russell). *1*. November 11, 1898.

BAIN (Robert Nisbet). *1*. April 24, 1896.

BALDENSPERGER (M. F.). *1*. December 14, 1921.

BALDWIN (Stanley), *1st Earl Baldwin of Bewdley*. *2*. February 20, 1923; January 14, 1926.

BALESTIER (Charles Wolcott) *to* LANE (John). *1*. October 21, 1890.

BALFOUR (Arthur James), *1st Earl of Balfour*. *26*. December 13, 1887—April 28, 1926. *Also 3* telegrams. July 15, 1900—June 12, 1906.

—— *to* ILBERT (*Sir* Courtenay Peregrine). *1*. June 22, 1918.

—— *to* WARD (Thomas Humphry). *1*. February 10, 1893.

—— *to* WEBSTER (Richard Everard), *1st Viscount Alverstone of Alverstone*. *1*. October 6, 1896.

—— *from* SYMONS (Rhoda) [Mrs. Arthur Symons]. *1*. October 22, [1908].

—— *see also* SHORT (Wilfrid Maurice) [*for* the Earl of Balfour].

BALFOUR (Elizabeth Edith), *Countess of Balfour. 1.* March 17, 1919.

BALFOUR (Gerald William), *2nd Earl of Balfour. 1.* March 21, 1892.

BALFOUR OF BURLEIGH (George John Gordon Bruce, *7th Baron), see* BRUCE (George John Gordon), *7th Baron Balfour of Burleigh.*

BALSILLIE (David) *to* HALDANE (Richard Burdon), *1st Viscount Haldane of Cloan. 1.* May 8, 1920.

BANCROFT (George). *3.* March 2, 1885—August 3, 1885.
Letter dated August 3, 1885: this is a transcript of the original, in Sir Edmund Gosse's hand.

BARING (Evelyn), *1st Earl of Cromer. 50.* July 29, 1909—June 6, 1916.

BARING (John), *2nd Baron Revelstoke of Revelstoke. 1.* December 2, 1919.

BARING (Maurice). *43.* April 9, 1894—August 12, 1925.
—— *to* GOSSE (Teresa). *1.* September 7, 1929.

BARING (Rowland Thomas), *2nd Earl of Cromer. 3.* June 27, 1918—January 30, 1923.

BARING (Thomas George), *1st Earl of Northbrook. 2.* June 15, 1904; August 13, 1904.

BARNARD (Frederick). *2.* September 17, 1896; 1 undated.

BARNES (John Gorell), *1st Baron Gorell of Brampton. 3.* February 11, 1909—September 27, 1909.

BARNES (Ronald Gorell), *3rd Baron Gorell of Brampton. 1.* January 1, 1925.

BARRÈS (Auguste Maurice). *4.* July, 1902—February, 1906.

BARRIE (*Sir* James Matthew), *1st Bart. 12.* January 11, 1898—October 5, 1927.

BARTLEET (Maud). *1.* July 25, 1922.

BARUZI (Jean). *1.* August 16, 1920.

BATEMAN (*Sir* Alfred Edmund). *4.* June 13, 1889—September 19, 1919.
—— *from* WOLFE (Humbert). *1.* May 7, 1928.

BATH (Thomas Henry Thynne, *5th Marquis of*), *see* THYNNE (Thomas Henry), *5th Marquis of Bath.*

BATHURST (L. J.). *1.* March 28, 1913.

BATHURST (Lilias Margaret Frances), *Countess Bathurst. 1.* February 6, [1914].

BATTERSEA (Constance Flower, *Baroness*), *see* FLOWER (Constance), *Baroness Battersea.*

BEARDSLEY (Aubrey Vincent). *1*. February 20, 1890.

BEARDSLEY (Ellen Agnes) [Mrs. Vincent Paul Beardsley].
1. January 11, [1897].

BEARDSLEY (Mabel). *1*. [March 21, 1898.]

BÉARN (B. de), *Comtesse*. *1*. [September 22, 1916.]

BEATTY (David), *1st Earl Beatty*. *3*. (December 24), 1919;
September 22, 1923; 1 undated.

BEAUCHAMP (Lettice Mary Elizabeth Lygon, *Countess*), *see*
LYGON (Lettice Mary Elizabeth), *Countess Beauchamp*.

BEAUCHAMP (William Lygon, *7th Earl*), *see* LYGON (William),
7th Earl Beauchamp.

BEAUCLERK (Grace), *Duchess of St. Albans*. *1*. December 12,
[1913].

BEAUNIER (André). *1*. October 19, 1922.

BECK (James M.). *1*. January 10, 1917.

BEDDOES (Thomas Pugh). *1*. June 11, 1925.

BEDFORD (Adeline Marie Russell, *Duchess of*), *see* RUSSELL
(Adeline Marie), *Duchess of Bedford*.

BEECHING (Henry Charles). *3*. [November 11 ? 1899]—
[November 15, 1899].

BEERBOHM (*Sir* Max). *22*. March 25, 1899—[November 24,
1917]; 3 undated.

—— *to* GOSSE (Ellen, *Lady*). *1*. March 19, 1929.

—— *to* SUNDAY TIMES. *1*. [May 18, 1928].

BEHRENS (A.). *1*. October 27, 1884.

BÉLARD (A.). *1*. January 5, 1904.

BELL (Henry Thomas Mackenzie). *1*. November 1, 1884.

BELL (John). *11*. October 11, 1881—July 3, 1889.

BELLOC (Bessie Rayner) [Mrs. Louis Swanton Belloc]. *6*.
July 19, 1894—[June 17, 1919].

BELLOC (Joseph Hilaire Pierre). *3*. July 13, 1909—
September 13, 1912.

BELLOWS (William). *4*. November 4, 1921—December 10,
1921.

—— *from* PANGE (*Comte* Jean de). *1*. November 4, 1921.

—— *from* PANGE (Pauline de), *Comtesse Jean de Pange*, *née*
de Broglie. *3*. August 26, 1921—November 11, 1925.

—— *from* SABATIER (Paul). *4*. July 29, 1921—January 9,
1922.

Letter of January 9, 1922: enclosed is a letter from Paul Sabatier to
Sir Edmund Gosse, dated October 14, 1916.

BENEDICT (Julius). *2*. March 16, 1882; October 18, 1887.

BENJAMIN (Lewis Saul), *pseud.* Lewis Melville, *from* SEAMAN
(*Sir* Owen), *1st Bart.* *1.* November 24, 1915.

BENN (Ernest) Ltd., *publishers.* *1.* December 16, 1925.

BENNETT (Enoch Arnold). *1.* February 27, 1905.

BENSON (Arthur Christopher). *27.* March 27, 1893—
August 3, 1924.
Letter of February 14, 1902: enclosed is part of a letter from Julian
Sturgis to A. C. Benson, dated February 13, [1902].

—— *to* CORNISH (Blanche Warre-) [Mrs. Francis Warre-
Cornish]. *1.* September 5, 1921.

—— *to* ROSS (A. G.). *1.* May 14, 1919.

—— *from* STURGIS (Julian). *1.* February 13, [1902].
Enclosed in a letter from A. C. Benson to Sir Edmund Gosse, dated
February 14, 1902. Incomplete. The signature is added in Sir Edmund
Gosse's hand.

BENSON (Dorothea Mary Roby), *Baroness Charnwood.* *2.*
September 19, 1919; August 12, 1925.

—— *from* PROTHERO (Rowland Edmund), *1st Baron Ernle of
Chelsea.* *1.* December 22, 1925.
Signed 'Ernle p.p. A. L. M.'

BENSON (Edward Frederic). *6.* October 7, 1893—May 3,
1927.

BENSON (Edward White), *Archbishop of Canterbury.* *1.*
January 13, (1896). *Also 2* telegrams. September 13,
1896; September 16, 1896.

—— *to* WEBSTER (Richard Everard), *1st Viscount Alverstone
of Alverstone.* *1.* September 15, 1896.
Transcript only.

BENSON (Godfrey Rathbone), *1st Baron Charnwood of Castle
Donington.* *3.* November 28, 1918—August 12, 1925.

BENSON (Mary) [Mrs. Edward White Benson]. *1.* April 10,
1895.

BENSON (Robert Hugh). *1.* Undated.

—— *from* GOSSE (*Sir* Edmund William). *1.* March 19, 1907.
A copy in Sir Edmund Gosse's hand.

BENTHAM (George). *1.* November 13, 1901.

BENTLEY (George). *2.* March 14, 1884; May 27, [1885].

BERESFORD (Charles William De la Poer), *1st Baron Beresford
of Metemmeh and Curraghmore, to* HALDANE (Richard
Burdon), *1st Viscount Haldane of Cloan.* *1.* July 8, 1917.

BERESFORD (Mina), *Baroness Beresford.* *4.* [March 19, 1920];
3 undated.

BERESTEIN (Henry). *1.* [April 9, 1927].

BERGER (Philippe). *1.* February 1, 1900.

BERNARD (John Henry). *2.* November 22, 1923; January 1, 1925.

BERNHARDT (Sarah) *from* GOSSE (*Sir* Edmund William). *1.* Undated.
Draft of first part only.

BERRY (James Gomer), *1st Viscount Kemsley of Dropmore.* *1* telegram. August 13, 1925.

BERRY (William Ewert), *1st Viscount Camrose of Hackwood Park.* *1.* June 8, 1921. *Also 1* telegram. August 13, 1925.

BESANT (*Sir* Walter). *3.* March 10, 1887—January 21, 1898.
—— *see also* GOSSE (*Sir* Edmund William) *and* BESANT (*Sir* Walter).

BIBESCO (Elizabeth Charlotte Lucy), *Princess, née* Asquith. *1.* May 3, 1919.

BIGELOW (Henry) *to* HARLAND (Aline) [Mrs. Henry Harland]. *1.* [*c.*1898].

BIGGE (*Sir* Lewis Amherst Selby-), *1st Bart., to* HALDANE (Richard Burdon), *1st Viscount Haldane of Cloan.* *1.* August 21, 1917.

BILDT (Carl Nils Daniel), *Baron de Bildt, to* KELLY (James Fitzmaurice-). *1.* May 12, 1919.

BILLE (Frank Ernest). *1.* January 14, 1912.

BINGHAM (George), *4th Earl of Lucan.* *2.* February 27, 1907; March 1, [1907 ?].

BINYON (Robert Laurence). *19.* November 29, 1910—January 1, 1925.

BIRKENHEAD (Frederick Edwin Smith, *1st Earl of*), *see* SMITH (Frederick Edwin), *1st Earl of Birkenhead.*

BIRRELL (Augustine). *11.* [July 8, 1889]—September 22, 1919; 1 undated.

BLAIKIE (John Arthur). *10.* June 10, 1868—November 16, 1910.
—— *to* GOSSE (Philip Henry). *1.* May 14, 1870.
—— *from* GOSSE (*Sir* Edmund William). *42.* March 13, 1868—March 23, 1874.

BLAKE (F. J. Aldrich). *2.* January 10, 1884; March 28, 1885.

BLANCHE (Jacques Émile). *3.* February 7, 1908; October 10, 1912; 1 undated.

BLUNDEN (Edmund Charles). *12.* December 27, 1922—February 15, 1928.

BODLEY (John Edward Courtenay). *1.* February 14, 1884.

BOËX-BOREL (Joseph Henri Honoré), *pseud.* J. H. Rosny *aîné, to* DAVRAY (Henry D.). *1* telegram. December 6, 1921.

BOLTON (Bertha L.). *2.* December 1, 1921; January 14, 1922.

BONE (*Sir* Muirhead). *2.* June 8, 1920; June 12, 1920.

BONHAM-CARTER (*Lady* Helen Violet), *née* Asquith, *see* ASQUITH (Helen Violet), *afterwards* Lady Helen Violet Bonham-Carter.

BONNIER (R. Albert). *1.* August 30, 1902.

BOOKER (Robert A. D.) [*for* Cosmo Gordon Lang, *Archbishop of York*] *to* Ross (A. G.). *1.* December 18, 1918.

BOOTH (Edwin) *to* HOWELLS [William Dean Howells?]. *1.* December 4, 1884.

BORDEAUX (Henry Camille). *3.* August 26, 1907—August 21, 1920.

BORENIUS (Tancred). *1.* August 12, 1925.

BOSANQUET (Bernard). *1.* February 12, 1909.

BOTTOMLEY (Gordon). *14.* August 18, 1915—January 28, 1920.

BOUGHTON (George Henry). *6.* March 22, 1883—April 1, 1896.

BOULMIER (Joseph). *1.* May 8, 1879.

BOULTON (*Sir* Harold Edwin), *2nd Bart., from* MILNES (Robert Offley Ashburton Crewe-), *1st Marquis of Crewe. 1.* June 7, 1922.

BOURGET (Paul Charles Joseph). *4.* April 11, 1897—January 24, 1901.

BOURKE (Dermot Robert Wyndham), *7th Earl of Mayo. 2.* July 6, 1901; August 3, 1909.

—— *from* ONSLOW (William Hillier), *4th Earl of Onslow. 1.* July 6, 1907.

BOUTROUX (Étienne Émile Marie). *5.* November 11, 1916—September 22, 1919; 1 undated.

BOUVERIE (Helen Matilda Pleydell-), *Countess of Radnor. 1.* February 28, 1902.

BOUVIER (Bernard). *2.* September 15, 1921; December 1, 1925.

BOWYER (Daphne), *Baroness Denham, née* Freeman-Mitford, *see* MITFORD (Daphne Freeman-), *afterwards* Baroness Denham.

BOYCE (George P.). *1.* February 13, 1884.

BOYD (Alice). *2*. May 3, 1873; May 6, 1873.

BOYLE (*Sir* Courtenay Edmund). *1*. February 11, 1898.

——*from* CHAPLIN (Henry), *1st Viscount Chaplin*. *1*. February 10, 1898.

BOYLESVE (René) *pseud*. [*i.e.* René Marie Auguste Tardiveau], *see* TARDIVEAU (René Marie Auguste), *pseud*. René Boylesve.

BRADDON (Mary Elizabeth), *afterwards* Mrs. John Maxwell. *3*. February 6, 1894—[June 27, 1894].

BRADLEY (Andrew Cecil). *3*. May 14, 1911; October 22, 1912; 1 undated.

—— *to* ARCHER (William). *2*. Undated.

BRADLEY (George Granville), *Dean of Westminster*. *1*. Undated.

BRADLEY (Kathleen Harris) *and* COOPER (Edith Emma), *pseud*. Michael Field, *to* SWINBURNE (Algernon Charles). *1*. [June 19, 1895].

BRAEKSTAD (Hans Lien). *1*. May 31, 1908.

BRAIN (Stuart). *1*. March 19, 1909.

BRANDES (Georg). *68*. June 9, 1873—December 25, 1913; 11 undated.

BRAYBROOKE (Patrick). *2*. August 11, 1925; June 19, 1926.

BRETT (John). *2*. January 13, 1884; August 25, 1886.

BRIDGES (Robert Seymour). *1*. January 8, 1878.

BRIGHTWEN (Eliza) *from* ALLEN (Phoebe). *3*. June 27, 1903—July 13, [1903].

BRITISH RED CROSS SOCIETY *and* ORDER OF ST. JOHN OF JERUSALEM IN ENGLAND, *Joint War Committee, see* HUDSON (*Sir* Robert Arundell) [*for* the Joint War Committee of the British Red Cross Society and the Order of St. John of Jerusalem in England].

BROCK (Arthur Clutton-). *2*. May 5, 1917; 1 undated.

BROGLIE (Pauline de), *afterwards* Comtesse Jean de Pange, *see* PANGE (Pauline de), *Comtesse Jean de Pange, née* de Broglie.

BROOKE (Margaret), *Ranee of Sarawak*. *2*. May 16, 1920; August 3, 1924. *Also 1* telegram. August 13, 1925.

BROOKE (Mary Ruth) [Mrs. William Parker Brooke]. *1*. April 30, 1915.

BROOKE (Rupert Chawner). *1*. July 27, 1913.

—— *from* GOSSE (*Sir* Edmund William). *2*. September 7, 1913; December 29, 1913.

BROOKE (Stopford Augustus). *6*. November 14, 1884—
February 21, 1916.

BROTHERTON (Edward Allen), *1st Baron Brotherton of Wakefield*
from TURNER (L. Godfrey). *1*. July 2, 1929.
  Enclosed: a letter from Sir Edmund Gosse to L. G. Turner, dated
  January 26, 1928.

BROUGHTON (Rhoda). *3*. January 26, [1897]; April 17,
1920; 1 undated.

BROWN (Ford Madox). *12*. April 6, 1871—June 30, 1884;
2 undated.

BROWN (Horatio Robert Forbes). *7*. January 16, 1894—
December 17, 1913.

BROWN (Marie Adelaide), *afterwards* Mrs. John B. Shipley.
1. November 19, 1882.

BROWN (Peter Hume). *1*. May 22, 1918.

BROWNE (Edward Granville). *1*. August 14, 1898.

BROWNE (George Forrest), *Bishop, first, of Stepney; afterwards,*
of Bristol. 3. February 6, 1905—October 28, 1915.

BROWNE (Henrietta L.). *1*. December 12, 1918.

BROWNING (Robert). *7*. January 22, 1872—February 20,
1889.

—— *to* GOSSE (Ellen, *Lady*). *2*. November 5, 1884; May 18,
1886.

BROWNING (Robert Wiedemann Barrett). *1*. January 24,
1890.

—— *from* GOSSE (*Sir* Edmund William). *2*. January 20,
1890; January 27, 1890.

BRUCE (George John Gordon), *7th Baron Balfour of Burleigh.*
1. July 10, 1922.

BRUNOT (Ferdinand) *from* MOCKEL (Albert). *1* telegram.
November 28, 1925.

BRYCE (James), *1st Viscount Bryce of Dechmont. 6*. July 12,
[1883]—May 1, 1917; 1 undated.

BUCHAN (John), *1st Baron Tweedsmuir of Elsfield. 1*. January
29, 1899.

BUCHANAN (*Sir* George William). *68*. November 17, 1919—
October 14, 1921; 1 undated.

—— *to* GOSSE (Ellen, *Lady*). *1*. Undated.

BUCKLE (George Earle). *5*. February 24, 1905—February
24, 1921.

BUCKMASTER (Stanley Owen), *1st Viscount Buckmaster of*
Cheddington. 3. June 22, 1924—March 18, 1926.

BUCKTON (George Bowdler). *1.* August 9, 1888.

BUDD (Charles Octavius). *1.* February 22, 1884.

BUISSON (Benjamin Paul). *1.* September 14, 1916.

BULLEN (Arthur Henry). *6.* September 30, 1887—August 24, 1892.

BULLER (*Lady* Audrey Jane Charlotte). *2.* December 4, 1899; December 16, 1901.

—— *to* KELLY (James Fitzmaurice-). *1.* May 9, 1919.

BULTEAU (*Mme. A.*), *pseuds.* Jacques Vontade; Fœmina. *17.* [October 21, 1912]—November 30, [1918]; 6 undated.

BURGE (Hubert Murray), *Bishop, first, of Southwark; afterwards, of Oxford.* *1.* July 12, [1911 ?].

BURGHCLERE (Herbert Coulstoun Gardner, *1st Baron*), *see* GARDNER (Herbert Coulstoun), *1st Baron Burghclere of Walden.*

BURGHCLERE (Winifred Anne Henrietta Christina Gardner, *Baroness*), *see* GARDNER (Winifred Anne Henrietta Christina), *Baroness Burghclere.*

BURNE-JONES (*Sir* Edward Coley), *1st Bart.* *3.* (June, 1885); 2 undated. *Also 1* telegram. February 6, 1894.

BURNE-JONES (*Sir* Philip), *2nd Bart.* *3.* July 13, 1915—December 14, 1916.

BURNETT (Frances Eliza Hodgson) [Mrs. Swan Moses Burnett], *afterwards* Mrs. Stephen Townesend. *4.* (September 1, 1889)—[February 10, 1890]; 1 undated.

BURROUGHS (John) *to* GILDER [Richard Watson Gilder ?]. *1.* Undated.

BURTON (*Sir* Frederic William). *3.* August 10, 1881—August 23, 1881.

BUTCHER (Samuel Henry). *5.* May 27, 1895—April 23, 1910.

BUTLER (Alfred Joshua). *1.* February 26, 1922.

BUTLER (Elizabeth, *Lady*). *1.* January 31, [1882].

BUTLER (Henry Montagu). *5.* December 14, 1886—October 13, 1909.

BUTLER (Nicholas Murray). *2.* August 26, 1914; June 27, 1917.

BUXTON (Sydney Charles), *1st Earl Buxton.* *1.* January 4, [1925 ?].

BYARD (Theodore). *1.* February 9, 1928.

BYWATER (Ingram). *2.* September 3, 1894; April 25, 1911.

C

CADDELL (W. W.). *1*. November 25, 1917.
> Enclosed, with suggested reply, in a letter from T. J. Wise to Sir Edmund Gosse, dated November 26, 1917.

CAINE (*Sir* Thomas Henry Hall). *8*. November 12, 1882—February 9, 1916; 2 undated.

—— *from* GOSSE (*Sir* Edmund William). *1*. November 27, 1882.

CALDERON (Philip H.). *1*. April 3, 1884.

CAMBON (Pierre Paul). *4*. October 31, 1913—September 12, 1916.

CAMERLYNCK (G.). *1*. October 14, 1925.

CAMMAERTS (Émile). *1*. May 6, [1916].

CAMPBELL (Beatrice Stella) [Mrs. Patrick Campbell], *afterwards* Mrs. George Frederick Myddleton Cornwallis-West. *3*. [January 26, 1895]—November 16, 1901.

CAMPBELL (Charles William). *1*. [1882].

CAMPBELL (Frederick Archibald Vaughan), *3rd Earl Cawdor of Castlemartin*. *1*. July 15, 1906.

CAMPBELL (Lewis). *1*. November 19, 1899.

CAMPBELL (Reginald John). *1*. September 25, 1915.

CAMROSE (William Ewert Berry, *1st Viscount*), *see* BERRY (William Ewert), *1st Viscount Camrose of Hackwood Park*.

CANE (Arthur Beresford). *1*. November 4, 1919.

—— *to* ROSS (A.G.). *1*. May 27, 1919.

CANTON (William). *3*. April 16, 1894—August 12, 1925.

CAREY (Fanny C.). *4*. July 24, 1901—September 11, 1902.

CARLISLE (George James Howard, *9th Earl of*), *see* HOWARD (George James), *9th Earl of Carlisle*.

CARNEGIE (Andrew). *2*. January 17, 1885; January 18, 1885.

CARR (Joseph William Comyns). *1*. July 16, 1915.

CARRINGTON (Charles Robert Wynn-), *1st Marquis of Lincolnshire*. *4*. February 3, 1913—January 17, 1925.

CARRINGTON (Rupert Clement George), *4th Baron Carrington of Upton*. *1*. August 13, 1925.

CARRUTHERS (Violet Rosa) [Mrs. James Carruthers]. *1*. August 12, 1925.

CARSON (Edward Henry), *1st Baron Carson of Duncairn*. *1*. [April 8, 1906].

CARTER (Jesse Benedict). *1*. January 9, 1908.

CASSELL AND CO., *publishers, see* FLOWER (*Sir* Walter Newman) [*for* Cassell and Co., *publishers*].

CAVAN (Frederick Rudolph Lambart, *10th Earl of*), *see* LAMBART (Frederick Rudolph), *10th Earl of Cavan.*

CAVENDISH (Evelyn), *Duchess of Devonshire. 1.* March 30, 1909.

CAVENDISH (William), *7th Duke of Devonshire. 4.* December 3, 1883—May 16, 1885.

CAWDOR (Frederick Archibald Vaughan Campbell, *3rd Earl*), *see* CAMPBELL (Frederick Archibald Vaughan), *3rd Earl Cawdor of Castlemartin.*

CECIL (Edgar Algernon Robert Gascoyne-), *1st Viscount Cecil of Chelwood. 1.* April 19, 1916.

CECIL (Hugh Richard Heathcote Gascoyne-), *1st Baron Quickswood of Clothall. 4.* December 2, 1914—March 12, 1925.

CHAMBERLAIN (Basil Hall). *2.* August 20, 1895; March 16, 1927.

CHAMBERLAIN (Beatrice Mary). *1.* June 28, 1906.

CHAMBERLAIN (*Sir* Joseph Austen). *16.* January 29, 1889—September 12, 1927.

——*from* GOSSE (*Sir* Edmund William). *1.* March 13, 1906.

CHAMBERLAIN (Mary E.) [Mrs. Joseph Chamberlain]. *1.* December 14, 1913.

CHAMBERS (Charles Haddon). *2.* [October 12, 1917]; August 9, [1920].

CHAMPNEYS (Basil). *2.* December 3, [1884?]; May 20, 1885.

CHANNING (Francis Allston), *1st Baron Channing of Wellingborough. 2.* November 14, 1912; October 21, 1914.

CHAPLIN (Henry), *1st Viscount Chaplin, to* BOYLE (*Sir* Courtenay Edmund). *1.* February 10, 1898.

CHAPMAN & HALL LTD., *publishers, see* WAUGH (Arthur) [*for* Chapman & Hall Ltd., *publishers*].

CHARLES (*Sir* Richard Havelock). *2.* September 22, 1919; [*c.* August 13, 1925].

CHARLÉTY (Sébastien). *6.* December 10, 1919—February 9, 1927; 1 undated. *Also 2* telegrams. November 19, 1921; November 25, 1921.

CHARNWOOD (Dorothea Mary Roby Benson, *Baroness*), *see* BENSON (Dorothea Mary Roby), *Baroness Charnwood.*

CHARNWOOD (Godfrey Rathbone Benson, *1st Baron*), *see*
BENSON (Godfrey Rathbone), *1st Baron Charnwood of
Castle Donington.*

CHARTERIS (*Sir* Evan Edward). *20.* [February 10, 1904]—
October 8, [1919]; 4 undated.

CHASE (Lewis Nathaniel). *2.* April 24, 1912; June 30, 1912.

CHESTERFIELD (Edwyn Francis Scudamore-Stanhope, *10th
Earl of*), *see* STANHOPE (Edwyn Francis Scudamore-),
10th Earl of Chesterfield.

CHEVALLEY (Abel Daniel). *3.* November 17, 1925—
December 3, 1925.

CHEVRILLON (André Louis). *7.* January 8, 1917—April 26,
1923; 3 undated.

CHICHESTER (Jocelyn Brudenell Pelham, *6th Earl of*), *see*
PELHAM (Jocelyn Brudenell), *6th Earl of Chichester.*

CHISHOLM (Hugh). *2.* January 1, 1909; September 22,
1919.

CHOLMONDELEY (Mary). *4.* April 5, 1902—February 29,
1904.

CHRISTENSEN (Carl). *1.* January 24, 1910.

CHURCHILL (Winston Leonard Spencer) *to* GOSSE (*Sir*
Edmund William) *and* GOSSE (Ellen, *Lady*). *1* telegram.
August 13, 1925.

CLARENDON (Edward Hyde Villiers, *5th Earl of*), *see* VILLIERS
(Edward Hyde), *5th Earl of Clarendon.*

CLARKE (George Sydenham), *1st Baron Sydenham of Combe.*
1. June 18, 1923.

CLEGHORN (John). *1.* October 27, 1884.

CLIFFORD (*Sir* Hugh). *3.* June 18, 1902—February 20, 1903.

CLIFFORD (Lucy) [Mrs. William Kingdon Clifford]. *3.*
[April 20, 1894]; June 23, 1913; 1 undated.

CLIVE (Robert George Windsor-), *1st Earl of Plymouth.* *1.*
December 25, 1908.

CLODD (Edward). *1.* August 12, 1925.

—— *from* DIXON (Charles). *1.* July 7, 1903.

Enclosed in a letter from Sir Edmund Gosse to Edward Clodd, dated
July 9, 1903.

—— *from* GOSSE (*Sir* Edmund William). *10.* March 23,
1886—January 2, 1925.

Letter dated July 9, 1903: enclosed is a letter from Charles Dixon to
Edward Clodd, dated July 7, 1903.

COHEN (Gustave). *1.* [September? 1924].

COLEBROOKE (Edward Arthur), *1st Baron Colebrooke of Stebun-heath*. *4*. June 16, 1909—December 9, 1911.

—— *and* HERSCHELL (Richard Farrer), *2nd Baron Herschell of Durham*. *1*. October 21, 1913.

COLLIER (John Payne). *1*. April 22, 1870.

COLLINS (John Churton). *5*. September 9, [1878]—June 26, 1879; 2 undated.

COLLINS (Richard Henn), *1st Baron Collins of Kensington*. *2*. July 10, 1907; 1 undated.

COLOMBI, *Marchesa, pseud.* [*i.e.* Mme. Eugenio Torelli-Viollier], *see* TORELLI-VIOLLIER (Maria) [Mme. Eugenio Torelli-Viollier], *pseud.* Marchesa Colombi.

COLVIN (*Sir* Sidney). *59*. September 18, 1872—August 13, 1925; 3 undated.

—— *to* [JAMES (Henry), *novelist ?*]. *1*. September 18, 1890.

—— *to* LANE (John). *1*. November 24, 1900.

—— *to* ROSS (A. G.). *1*. [*c.* November 30, 1918].

—— *to* THOMPSON (William Hepworth). *1*. April 22, 1883.

—— *from* MORLEY (John), *1st Viscount Morley of Blackburn*. *1*. February 8, 1883.

COMPTON (William George Spencer Scott), *5th Marquis of Northampton*. *2*. May 27, 1892; February 11, 1903.

CONRAD (Joseph) *to* ROSS (A. G.). *1*. May 9, 1919.

CONWAY (William Martin), *1st Baron Conway of Allington*. *2*. September 25, 1896; November 12, 1922.

COOPER (Constance Sibell Ashley-), *Countess of Shaftesbury*. *1*. April 22, [1909].

COOPER (Edith Emma), *see* BRADLEY (Kathleen Harris) *and* COOPER (Edith Emma), *pseud.* Michael Field.

COPEAU (A. L.) [Mme. Jacques Copeau]. *1*. November 15, 1911.

COPEAU (Jacques). *3*. October 14, 1911—July 23, 1912.

CORNISH (Blanche Warre-) [Mrs. Francis Warre-Cornish]. *1*. October 22, [1921].

—— *from* BENSON (Arthur Christopher). *1*. September 5, 1921.

CORNWALLIS-WEST (Beatrice Stella) [Mrs. George Frederick Myddleton Cornwallis-West], *formerly* Mrs. Patrick Campbell, *see* CAMPBELL (Beatrice Stella) [Mrs. Patrick Campbell], *afterwards* Mrs. George Frederick Myddleton Cornwallis-West.

COTTING (B. E.). *1*. June 17, 1884.

COUPERUS (Louis). *2.* February 15, 1891; February 27, 1891.

COURT (M. F.). *2.* August 12, 1925; August 6, 1926.

COURTHOPE (William John). *11.* February 8, 1884—
January 10, 1905.

COURTNEY (Leonard Henry), *1st Baron Courtney of Penwith. 2.*
May 16, 1907; [January 7], 1912.

COWPER (Francis Thomas de Grey), *7th Earl Cowper. 1.*
December 11, 1902.

COWPER (Katrine Cecilia), *Countess Cowper. 1.* Undated.

Cox (Harold). *3.* September 14, 1915—September 21,
1919.

CRACKANTHORPE (Hubert). *1.* January 23, [1894].

CRAIGIE (Pearl Mary Teresa) [Mrs. Reginald Walpole
Craigie], *pseud.* John Oliver Hobbes. *20.* January 14,
1898—June 5, 1905.

—— *from* GOSSE (*Sir* Edmund William). *1.* June 30, 1899.
Typewritten copy only.

CRAWFORD AND BALCARRES (David Alexander Edward
Lindsay, *Earl of*), *see* LINDSAY (David Alexander
Edward), *27th Earl of Crawford and 10th Earl of Balcarres.*

CREIGHTON (Louise) [Mrs. Mandell Creighton]. *1.*
Undated.

CREIGHTON (Mandell), *Bishop, first, of Peterborough; afterwards,
of London. 9.* May 18, 1885—October 6, 1899.

CREWE (Robert Offley Ashburton Crewe-Milnes, *1st Marquis
of*), *see* MILNES (Robert Offley Ashburton Crewe-),
1st Marquis of Crewe.

CRIPPS (Charles Alfred), *1st Baron Parmoor of Frieth. 1.*
August 4, 1914.

CROCKETT (Samuel Rutherford). *4.* April 2, 1894—June
15, 1894.

CROMER (Evelyn Baring, *1st Earl of*), *see* BARING (Evelyn),
1st Earl of Cromer.

CROMER (Rowland Thomas Baring, *2nd Earl of*), *see* BARING
(Rowland Thomas), *2nd Earl of Cromer.*

CROZIER (John Baptist), *Archbishop of Armagh and Primate of
all Ireland. 2.* February 6, 1911; November 5, 1915.

CUFFE (Hamilton John Agmondesham), *5th Earl of Desart.*
4. September 2, 1918—January 10, [1925].

CUMING (Hugh) *from* GOSSE (Philip Henry). *8.* January 23,
1845—January 27, 1846.
Duplicate copies only.

CURRAN (Minnie B.). *3*. December 5, 1898—July 15, 1899.

CURTIS (George William). *1*. January 14, 1885.

—— *to* HARPER ( ). *1*. December 29, 1884.

CURZON (George Nathaniel), *1st Marquis Curzon of Kedleston.*
60. May 28, 1893—December 16, 1924; 2 undated.

——*and others*. *1*. February 29, 1912.

CUST (*Sir* Lionel Henry). *3*. August 13, 1925—May 13, 1927.

D

DAMES (Mansel L.). *3*. April 26, 1874; 2 undated.
Of the two undated letters, one is incomplete (last two leaves only).

DARLING (Charles John), *1st Baron Darling of Langham*. *5*.
May 27, [1918]; 4 undated.

DARMESTETER (Agnes Mary Frances), *née* Robinson [Mme.
James Darmesteter], *afterwards* Mme. Pierre Émile
Duclaux, *see* ROBINSON (Agnes Mary Frances), *after-
wards* Mme. James Darmesteter, *afterwards* Mme.
Pierre Émile Duclaux.

DARTMOUTH (William Heneage Legge, *6th Earl of*), *see* LEGGE
(William Heneage), *6th Earl of Dartmouth.*

DARWIN (Charles Robert) *to* GOSSE (Philip Henry). *2*.
April 27, [1857]; [June 2, 1863].

DARWIN (*Sir* Francis). *2*. February 12, 1912; November 22,
1919.

DARWIN (*Sir* George Howard). *4*. November 13, 1899—
March 21, 1901; 1 undated.

DAVIDSON (James Leigh Strachan-). *1*. November 24, 1896.

DAVIDSON (John). *10*. July 3, 1895—January 29, 1901.

—— *to* M'CORMICK (*Sir* William Symington). *1*. February
12, 1901.

DAVIDSON (Randall Thomas), *1st Baron Davidson of Lambeth,
Archbishop of Canterbury*. *9*. March 8, 1904—November
4, 1916.

DAVIES (David). *10*. March 22, 1915—July 14, 1915.

DAVIS (John). *1*. January 9, 1884.

DAVRAY (Henry D.). *20*. October 14, 1903—November 25,
1925.

—— *from* BOËX-BOREL (Joseph Henri Honoré), *pseud.* J. H.
Rosny *aîné. 1* telegram. December 6, 1921.

—— *from* HEREDIA (José Maria de). *1*. (February 5, 1904).

DAWSON (Geoffrey) *to* HALDANE (Richard Burdon), *1st Viscount Haldane of Cloan*. *1*. December 13, 1918.

DEANE (John Bathurst). *2*. January 14, 1884; January 16, [1884].

DE BUNSEN (*Sir* Maurice William Ernest), *1st Bart*. *1*. September 21, 1919.

DE GREY (Thomas), *6th Baron Walsingham of Walsingham*. *1*. February 10, 1884.

DE LA MARE (Walter John). *2*. March 23, 1915; July 12, 1927. *Also 2* telegrams. March 23, 1915; August 13, 1925.

DELATTRE (Floris). *1*. November 22, 1913.

DEMOLDER (Eugène). *1*. [August 17, 1916].

DENHAM (Daphne Bowyer, *Baroness*), *see* MITFORD (Daphne Freeman-), *afterwards* Baroness Denham.

DERBY (Edward Henry Stanley, *15th Earl of*), *see* JUST (H. W.) [*for* Edward Henry Stanley, *15th Earl of Derby*].

DESART (Hamilton John Agmondesham Cuffe, *5th Earl of*), *see* CUFFE (Hamilton John Agmondesham), *5th Earl of Desart*.

DE SAUMAREZ (James St. Vincent Saumarez, *4th Baron*), *see* SAUMAREZ (James St. Vincent), *4th Baron de Saumarez of Saumarez*.

DESBOROUGH (Ethel Anne Priscilla Grenfell, *Baroness*), *see* GRENFELL (Ethel Anne Priscilla), *Baroness Desborough*.

DESBOROUGH (William Henry Grenfell, *1st Baron*), *see* GRENFELL (William Henry), *1st Baron Desborough of Taplow*.

DESJARDINS (Paul). *7*. August 12, 1911—November 13, 1914.

DE TABLEY (John Byrne Leicester Warren, *3rd Baron*), *see* WARREN (John Byrne Leicester), *3rd Baron de Tabley*.

DE VERE (Aubrey Thomas). *4*. July 11, 1896—March 14, 1898.

DEVEREUX (Robert), *16th Viscount Hereford*. *3*. December 25, 1905—March 31, 1911.

DEVONSHIRE (Evelyn Cavendish, *Duchess of*), *see* CAVENDISH (Evelyn), *Duchess of Devonshire*.

DEVONSHIRE (William Cavendish, *7th Duke of*), *see* CAVENDISH (William), *7th Duke of Devonshire*.

DICKINS (Philip). *9*. October 3, 1923—March 4, 1927.

DICKSEE (*Sir* Francis Bernard). *14*. November 27, [1883]—June 12, 1926; 1 undated.

—— *to* Ross (A.G.). *1.* January 25, 1919.

Dickson-Poynder (John Poynder), *1st Baron Islington of Islington*. *3.* March 4, 1918—November 11, 1920.

Dilke (*Sir* Charles Wentworth), *2nd Bart.* *1.* May 5, [1885].

Dimnet (Ernest). *1.* Undated.

Ditchfield (Peter Hampson). *1.* January 20, 1918.

Dixon (Charles) *to* Clodd (Edward). *1.* July 7, 1903.
Enclosed in a letter from Sir Edmund Gosse to Edward Clodd, dated July 9, 1903.

Dixon (Richard Watson). *6.* September 20, 1883—April 25, 1893.

Dobell (Bertram). *1.* October 22, 1912.

Dobson (A. Mary R.). *1.* September 4, 1921.

Dobson (Alban Tabor Austin). *3.* January 15, 1922—July 13, 1926.

—— *to* Gosse (Philip). *1.* March 19, 1934.

Dobson (Frances Mary) [Mrs. Henry Austin Dobson]. *1.* July 23, 1921.

—— *to* Gosse (*Sir* Edmund William) *and* Gosse (Ellen, *Lady*). *1.* September 18, 1919.

Dobson (Henry Austin). *345.* August 25, 1874—September 8, [1921].

—— *to* Gosse (Philip). *1.* (December 10, 1897).

—— *to* Kelly (James Fitzmaurice-). *1.* December 21, 1918.

—— *to* Pelham (Thomas Henry William). *1.* January 17, 1898.

Dodson (John William), *2nd Baron Monk Bretton of Conyboro and Hurstpierpoint*. *2.* July 29, 1914; 1 undated.

Donoughmore (Richard Walter John Hely-Hutchinson, *6th Earl of*), *see* Hely-Hutchinson (Richard Walter John), *6th Earl of Donoughmore*.

Doubleday (Edward) *from* Gosse (Philip Henry). *1.* July 16, 1845.

Douglas (*Sir* George Brisbane Scott-), *5th Bart.* *9.* January 11, [1896]—[August] 3, [1921]; 1 undated. *Also 1* telegram. August 13, 1925.

Doulton (*Sir* Henry). *2.* December 1, 1883; March 17, 1885.

Doulton (Henry Lewis). *5.* July 1, 1898—May 21, 1900.

Doumic (René). *3.* May 16, 1916—September 18, 1923.

DOWDEN (Edward). *35.* February 12, 1877—November 16, 1911.
—— *to* WOLSELEY, *Lady* [Louisa, Viscountess Wolseley ?]. *1.* February 1, 1895.
—— *from* GOSSE (*Sir* Edmund William). *1.* May 16, 1893.
DOWDEN (Elizabeth Dickinson) [Mrs. Edward Dowden]. *1.* November 9, 1913.
DOYLE (*Sir* Arthur Conan). *2.* [January ? 1898]; 1 undated.
DRACHMANN (Holger Henrik Herholdt). *3.* November 7, [1874]—December 15, 1900.
DRINKWATER (John). *22.* April 7, 1913—December 15, 1920.
DU BOS (Charles). *1.* November 23, 1925.
DUCHESNE (Louis). *2.* July 10, 1887; July 25, 1887.
DUCLAUX (Agnes Mary Frances) [Mme. Pierre Émile Duclaux], *formerly* Mme. James Darmesteter, *née* Robinson, *see* ROBINSON (Agnes Mary Frances), *afterwards* Mme. James Darmesteter, *afterwards* Mme. Pierre Émile Duclaux.
DUFF (*Lady* Gladys Mary Juliet). *1.* July 19, [1915].
DUFF (*Sir* Mountstuart Elphinstone Grant). *2.* October 28, 1900; October 13, 1903.
DU MAURIER (George Louis Palmella Busson). *2.* April 12, [1883]; April 20, [1883].
DUMUR (Louis). *1.* May 9, 1923.
DUNCOMBE (Charles William Reginald), *2nd Earl of Feversham.* *1.* June 27, 1904.
DUNEDIN (Andrew Graham Murray, *1st Viscount*), *see* MURRAY (Andrew Graham), *1st Viscount Dunedin.*
DUNTHORNE (Robert). *1.* February 6, 1884.
DUTT (Govin Chunder). *1.* October 3, 1879.
DYER (*Sir* William Turner Thiselton-). *4.* January 1, 1896— October 20, 1907.

E

EAST (*Sir* Alfred). *4.* May 11, 1903—June 24, 1910; 1 undated.
ECCLES (Francis Yvon). *3.* January 21, 1913—December 25, [1920].
EDGCUMBE (William Henry), *4th Earl of Mount Edgcumbe. 3.* November 22, 1910—December 23, 1910.

EDGREN (Anne Charlotte Gustava), *née* Leffler [fru G. E. Edgren], *afterwards* Duchèssa di Cajanello, *see* LEFFLER (Anne Charlotte Gustava), *afterwards* fru G. E. Edgren, *afterwards* Duchèssa di Cajanello.

EDMONDS (Elizabeth M.). *5.* April 28, 1902—October 22, 1902; 1 undated.

EEDEN (Frederik van). *6.* October 7, 1890—December 14, 1891.

EGGERS (Olga). *1.* Undated.

EGLINTON (John) *pseud.* [*i.e.* William Kirkpatrick Magee], *see* MAGEE (William Kirkpatrick), *pseud.* John Eglinton.

EGLINTON AND WINTON (Archibald Seton Montgomerie, *16th Earl of*), *see* MONTGOMERIE (Archibald Seton), *16th Earl of Eglinton and Winton.*

EINARSSON (Indridi). *1.* August 14, 1905.

ELGAR (*Sir* Edward). *1.* August 7, 1925.

ELLICOTT (Charles John), *Bishop, first, of Gloucester and Bristol; afterwards, of Gloucester. 4.* December 4, 1883—January 25, 1896.

ELLIOT (Arthur Ralph Douglas). *1.* May 7, 1912.

ELLIOTT (Frank). *1.* September 15, 1916.

ELLIS (Thomas Evelyn Scott-), *8th Baron Howard de Walden. 1.* December 26, 1912.

ELTON (Oliver). *8.* November 30, 1920—October 8, 1927.

EMERSON (Ralph Waldo). *1.* March 5, 1882.

ENGLISH ASSOCIATION, *see* HOUGHTON (A. V.) [*for* the English Association].

ERNLE (Rowland Edmund Prothero, *1st Baron*), *see* PROTHERO (Rowland Edmund), *1st Baron Ernle of Chelsea.*

ESCHOLIER (Raymond). *2.* May 2, 1920; December 20, 1920.

EVANS (Charles Seddon). *4.* September 19, 1919—September 1, 1922; 1 undated [incomplete].

EVERSLEY (George John Shaw-Lefevre, *1st Baron*), *see* SHAW-LEFEVRE (George John), *1st Baron Eversley of Old Ford, London.*

EWALD (Herman Frederik). *1.* March 14, 1878.

F

FAIRBAIRN (Andrew Martin). *2.* May 21, 1899; May 29, 1899.

FARADAY (Paul). *1.* August 24, 1926.

FARRER (Thomas Cecil), *2nd Baron Farrer of Abinger*. *3.* July 25, 1913 [2]; July 26, 1913.

FARRER (Thomas Henry), *1st Baron Farrer of Abinger*. *7.* August 13, 1884—September 14, 1884.

—— *from* GOSSE (*Sir* Edmund William). *1.* September 8, 1884.
Rough draft.

FAWCETT (Henry). *1.* January 10, 1884.

FERRUGGIA (Gemma). *1.* January 23, 1928.

FEVERSHAM (Charles William Reginald Duncombe, *2nd Earl of*), *see* DUNCOMBE (Charles William Reginald), *2nd Earl of Feversham.*

FIELD (Eugene). *1.* October 16, 1890.

FIELD (Michael) *pseud.* [*i.e.* Kathleen Harris Bradley *and* Edith Emma Cooper], *see* BRADLEY (Kathleen Harris) *and* COOPER (Edith Emma), *pseud.* Michael Field.

FILDES (*Sir* Luke). *3.* August 15, 1881—December 25, 1882.

FILON (Augustin). *1.* November 6, [1900].

FIRTH (*Sir* Charles Harding) *to* HUNT (William). *1.* June 30, 1901.
Enclosed in a letter from William Hunt to Sir Edmund Gosse, dated July 2, 1901.

FISHER (A. Hugh). *1.* July 1, 1917.

FISHER (Adrienne) *to* ROSS (A. G.) *1.* May 8, 1919.

FISHER (Herbert Albert Laurens). *21.* February 23, 1904—November 5, 1927; 1 undated.

FITCH (*Sir* Joshua Girling). *1.* December 6, 1883.

FITZMAURICE (Edmond George Petty), *1st Baron Fitzmaurice of Leigh*. *5.* March 9, 1906—January 25, 1925.

FITZMAURICE (Henry Charles Keith Petty), *5th Marquis of Lansdowne*. *7.* March 12, [1907]—March 3, 1916.

FLEURIAU (Aimé Joseph de). *7.* November 17, 1913—March 30, 1926.

FLOWER (Constance), *Baroness Battersea*. *1.* March 1, [1914].

FLOWER (*Sir* Walter Newman) [*for* Cassell and Co., *publishers*]. *1.* November 5, 1921.

FŒMINA, *pseud.* [*i.e.* Mme. A. Bulteau], *see* BULTEAU (Mme. A.), *pseuds.* Jacques Vontade; Fœmina.

FOG (Bruun Juul), *Bishop, first, of Aarhus ; afterwards, of Sjælland, from* ANDERSEN (Hans Christian). *1.* May 13, 1874.

FONTAINAS (André). *4.* October 23, 1913—January 27, 1920.

FORBES (Bernard Arthur William Patrick Hastings), *8th Earl of Granard*. *2*. Undated.

FORT (Paul). *5*. July 10, 1902—September 21, 1923; 1 undated.

FORTESCUE (George Knottesford). *1*. February 18, 1896.

FOSTER (*Sir* Gregory). *1*. September 27, 1919.

FOUNTAIN CLUB. *1*. January 16, 1925.

FOWLER (T.). *1*. April 22, 1888.

FOX-STRANGWAYS (Giles Stephen Holland), *6th Earl of Ilchester*. *1*. May 8, [1925].

—— *see also* FOX-STRANGWAYS (Helen Mary Theresa), *Countess of Ilchester, and* FOX-STRANGWAYS (Giles Stephen Holland), *6th Earl of Ilchester*.

FOX-STRANGWAYS (Helen Mary Theresa), *Countess of Ilchester*. *2*. October 20, [1919]; August 12, 1925.

—— *and* FOX-STRANGWAYS (Giles Stephen Holland), *6th Earl of Ilchester*. *1*. January 4, [1925].

FRAMPTON (*Sir* George James). *1*. [December 17, 1913].

—— *to* Ross (A. G.) *1*. May 10, 1919.

FRANCE, *Ministère des Affaires Étrangères, Service de l'Information Diplomatique*. *1*. September 19, 1916.

FRANTZEN (J. J. A. A.) [*for the Maatschappij der Nederlandsche Letterkunde te Leiden*]. *2*. July 5, 1878; 1 undated.

FRAZER (*Sir* James George). *39*. May 10, 1895—January 11, 1925.

—— *to* Ross (A. G.) *1*. September 27, 1919.

FRAZER (Lilly, *Lady*), *formerly* Mrs. Grove. *3*. October 5, 1904—June 25, 1910.

FREEMAN (John). *1*. June 18, 1924.

FRESHFIELD (Douglas William). *2*. March 16, 1910; April 19, 1910.

FROUDE (James Anthony). *1*. January 27, [1881].

FURNESS (Horace Howard). *25*. January 12, 1885—May 24 [1908]; 8 undated.

—— [*for the Penn Club*]. *1*. December 22, 1884.

FURNIVALL (Frederick James). *1*. October 15, 1879.

—— *to* WRIGHT (William Aldis). *1*. February 28, 1905.

FURTADO (Joseph). *13*. March 23, 1921—August 26, 1927.

—— *from* GOSSE (*Sir* Edmund William). *1*. February 15, 1925.
Draft or copy.

FURTADO (Philip). *1*. April 28, 1927.

G

GAIRDNER (James). *1*. April 21, 1907.

GALSWORTHY (John). *2*. March 23, 1908; September 11, 1927.

GALTON (Arthur). *1*. December 14, 1902.

GARDINER (Samuel Rawson). *6*. November 28, 1883— November 29, 1885.

GARDNER (Herbert Coulstoun), *1st Baron Burghclere of Walden*. *44*. February 21, 1893—July 28, 1919; 4 undated.

GARDNER (Thomas A.) [*for* the *Sunday Times*]. *1*. January 5, 1924.

GARDNER (Winifred Anne Henrietta Christina), *Baroness Burghclere*. *21*. February 8, 1901—December 25, 1913.
Letter of December 25, 1913: enclosed is a letter from Constance, Baroness Leconfield, dated December 20, [1913]. The letter dated May 7, 1903, is incomplete.

—— *from* WYNDHAM (Constance Evelyn), *Baroness Leconfield*. *1*. December 20 [1913].
Enclosed in a letter from Lady Burghclere to Sir Edmund Gosse, dated 'Xmas Day, 1913.'

GARNETT (Edward). *5*. February 14, 1911—February 24, 1911; 1 dated ' February, 1911.'

GARNETT (Richard). *17*. April 24, (1877)—March 16, 1905.

—— *to* LANE (John). *1*. March 16, 1895.

GARNIER (Charles Marie). *2*. October 3, 1916; October 1, 1919.

GARVIN (James Louis). *1*. March 23, 1922.

GASELEE (*Sir* Stephen). *1*. November 6, 1925.

GAULTIER (Jules de). *1*. [September 27?] (1918).

GEIJERSTAM (Gustaf af). *1*. December 1, 1902.

GEIKIE (*Sir* Archibald). *3*. March 10, 1905—October 25, 1905.

GEORGE II, *King of the Hellenes*. *1*. October 9, 1916.

GIDE (André Paul Guillaume). *6*. June 5, 1915—April 8, 1928.
Three of the letters, dated June 5—July 19, 1915, are typewritten copies.

—— *to* GOSSE (Philip). *5*. February 8, 1929—May 2, 1930.

GILBERT (Alfred). *3*. January 16, 1887—February 9, 1887.

GILDER (Richard Watson). *2*. November 1, 1886; June 25, 1912.

—— *see also* BURROUGHS (John) *to* GILDER [Richard Watson Gilder?].

After of Searby's engraved portraits of Napoleon & Marie Louise by EJ.

1, Carlton House Terrace,
S.W.1.

May 22 18

My dear Grove

A new friends
act ! Yes.)
Collect these
things for ultimate
gift 8 the nation
and shall be
delighted & have
your valuable contribution.

Yours CURZON

Letter from the Marquis Curzon of Kedleston

University College, London
19 Jan. 1911

My dear Gosse,

Many thanks for your kind letter. In most respects, though not quite in all, I think the change is matter for congratulation. If the exhalations of the Granta give me a relaxed sore throat, more poems may be expected.

Yours sincerely
A. E. Housman.

Letter from A. E. Housman

34 De Vere Gardens W.

H. Metropole Brighton

My dear Gosse.

...& I am covered with shame as with a garment & with contrition as with a leprosy. I haven't had the courage — these 24 hours — to tell you that yesterday, in a crisis of confusion, I managed to lose the paper containing your beautiful address

I shall probably return to town in a day or two. Yours always Henry James

First page of a letter from Henry James

La bonne année!

15 Fitzroy Street
Jan 2. 1924

My dear Gosse

Under a confused Christmas impression I opened your box expecting to find Casabel plumes tho a parterre of Flor de Cuba Magnificos Imperiales Rothschild!

I smoked with close attention close and grateful attention, & was meditating & jotting terms of acknowledgment.

Unfortunately for the cigar your book on English literature was in my hand, so that I am diverted into the impertinence of thanking you for having written it. And I had never seen it before! Jacques Blanche used to say "La lecture délicate dépend entièrement du hasard. De petit cabinet." It really is a thinking book, a concentration of your precious qualities of clarity, brevity, modesty & wit. "Brevitatis artifex" has always seemed to me the highest praise. And you are witty, not for the sake of being witty, but every stroke of your wit carries your theme ahead with a bound, as a good painter steers with every stroke. I am reading it again & shall I hope often do so. I am a good dog to try just such a book, being ignorant, critical and avid to learn. Affectionately yours Walter Sickert —

Letter from Walter Sickert

GILES (Herbert Allen). *2.* September 28, 1899; May 10, 1911.

GILLET (Louis). *8.* November 12, 1921—December 8, 1925.

GISSING (Algernon). *2.* April 15, 1904; 1 undated.

—— *to* WELLS (Herbert George). *1.* May 28, 1912.

GJELLERUP (Karl Adolf). *1.* May 20, 1882.

GLADSTONE (Helen). *1.* March 2, 1892.

GLAISHER (James Whitbread Lee). *1.* February 28, 1910.

GLEICHEN (*Countess* Feodora). *5.* December 17, 1902—September 21, 1919; 2 undated.

GODLEY (John Arthur), *1st Baron Kilbracken of Killegar. 2.* November 10, 1909; March 2, 1911.

GODWIN (Fanny Bryant) *to* GOSSE (Ellen, *Lady*). *1.* December 13, [1884].

—— *from* GOSSE (Ellen, *Lady*). *1.* [December, 1884?].
Draft, in the handwriting of Sir Edmund Gosse, of reply to Mrs. Godwin's letter to Lady Gosse, dated December 13, [1884]. Unsigned.

GOLDSCHMIDT (Meir Aaron). *1.* January 27, 1877.

GOLLANCZ (*Sir* Israel). *2.* May 22, 1919; August 20, 1922.

GOODWIN (Harvey), *Bishop of Carlisle. 1.* December 3, 1883.

GORDON (Arthur Hamilton-), *1st Baron Stanmore of Great Stanmore. 7.* November 7, 1905—March 3, [1910]; 1 undated.

GORDON (George Arthur Maurice Hamilton-), *2nd Baron Stanmore of Great Stanmore. 1.* February 21, 1912.

GORDON (George Stuart). *1.* June 6, 1927.

GORDON (John Campbell), *1st Marquis of Aberdeen and Temair. 1.* May 17, 1908.

GORE (Arthur Jocelyn Charles), *6th Earl of Arran. 1.* February 19, 1914.

GORE (Charles), *Bishop, first, of Worcester; afterwards, of Birmingham; afterwards, of Oxford. 3.* July 13, 1907—[*c.* August 10, 1925].

GORELL (John Gorell Barnes, *1st Baron*), *see* BARNES (John Gorell), *1st Baron Gorell of Brampton.*

GORELL (Ronald Gorell Barnes, *3rd Baron*), *see* BARNES (Ronald Gorell), *3rd Baron Gorell of Brampton.*

GOSCHEN (George Joachim), *1st Viscount Goschen of Hawkhurst. 1.* July 14, [1905].

GOSFORD (Archibald Brabazon Sparrow Acheson, *4th Earl of*), *see* ACHESON (Archibald Brabazon Sparrow), *4th Earl of Gosford.*

GOSSE (Edmund B.). *1.* November 11, 1925.

GOSSE (*Sir* Edmund William) *to* BENSON (Robert Hugh). *1.* March 19, 1907.
A copy, in Sir Edmund Gosse's hand.

—— *to* BERNHARDT (Sarah). *1.* Undated.
Draft of first part only.

—— *to* BLAIKIE (John Arthur). *42.* March 13, 1868— March 23, 1874.

—— *to* BROOKE (Rupert Chawner). *2.* September 7, 1913; December 29, 1913.

—— *to* BROWNING (Robert Wiedemann Barrett). *2.* January 20, 1890; January 27, 1890.

—— *to* CAINE (*Sir* Thomas Henry Hall). *1.* November 27, 1882.

—— *to* CHAMBERLAIN (*Sir* Joseph Austen). *1.* March 13, 1906.

—— *to* CLODD (Edward). *10.* March 23, 1886—January 2, 1925.
Letter dated July 9, 1903: enclosed is a letter from Charles Dixon to Edward Clodd, dated July 7, 1903.

—— *to* CRAIGIE (Pearl Mary Teresa) [Mrs. Reginald Walpole Craigie], *pseud.* John Oliver Hobbes. *1.* June 30, 1899.
Typewritten copy only.

—— *to* DOWDEN (Edward). *1.* May 16, 1893.

—— *to* FARRER (Thomas Henry), *1st Baron Farrer of Abinger.* *1.* September 8, 1884.
Rough Draft.

—— *to* FURTADO (Joseph). *1.* February 15, 1925.
Draft or copy.

—— *to* HARCOURT (Lewis), *1st Viscount Harcourt of Stanton Harcourt.* *1.* [March 24, 1908].
Rough draft, unsigned.

—— *to* HUDSON (Frederic). *2.* November 2, 1895; October 8, 1896.

—— *to* HUTTON (Richard Holt). *1.* March 10, 1893.
Typewritten, including signature. Copy?

—— *to* IBSEN (Henrik). *1.* March 17, 1898.
Draft.

—— *to* JONES (Henry Arthur). *11.* October 11, 1889— September 16, 1925.

—— *to* MILNES (Robert Offley Ashburton Crewe-), *1st Marquis of Crewe.* *1.* Undated.

—— *to* SCHWARTZ (Joost Marius Willem van der Poorten-), *pseud.* Maarten Maartens. *1.* December 27, 1898.
Typewritten copy.

—— *to* SHORTER (Clement King). *95.* July 20, 1887—February 16, 1916; 4 undated.

—— *to* SWINBURNE (Algernon Charles). *2.* November 19, 1880; March 2, 1881.

—— *to* TURNER (L. Godfrey). *1.* January 26, 1928.
Enclosed in a letter from L. G. Turner to Lord Brotherton, dated July 2, 1929.

—— *to* VANE-TEMPEST-STEWART (Theresa Susey Helen), *Marchioness of Londonderry.* *1.* February 9, 1914.
A copy, in Sir Edmund Gosse's hand.

—— *to* WATSON (Robinson). *1.* March 10, 1893.

—— *to* WATSON (*Sir* William). *14.* June 21, 1880—December 15, 1916.
All except one, dated February 27, 1882, are typewritten transcripts.

—— *to* WATTS (Walter Theodore), *afterwards* Watts-Dunton. *27.* May 4, 1876—May 31, 1902; 5 undated.
The letter dated October 2, 1879 is a typewritten copy.

—— *to* WISE (Thomas James). *398.* June 21, 1893—February 25, 1928; 2 undated.
Also part of a letter in Sir Edmund Gosse's hand, signed, with postscript—presumably to Wise; undated.
Letters of May 25 and 26, 1915: enclosed are two letters from Isabel Swinburne to T. J. Wise, dated May 22 and May 24.

—— *to* WOLSELEY (Garnet Joseph), *1st Viscount Wolseley.* *1.* June 30, 1889.

—— *and* BESANT (*Sir* Walter) *from* JAMES (Henry), *novelist.* *1.* July 12, [1888].

—— *and* GOSSE (Ellen, *Lady*) *from* CHURCHILL (Winston Leonard Spencer). *1* telegram. August 13, 1925.

—— *and* GOSSE (Ellen, *Lady*) *from* DOBSON (Frances Mary) [Mrs. Henry Austin Dobson]. *1.* September 18, 1919.

—— *and* GOSSE (Ellen, *Lady*) *from* JAMES (Henry), *novelist.* *2.* October 14, 1907; [December 29, 1908].

—— *and* GOSSE (Ellen, *Lady*) *from* JONES (Loe) *and* JONES (Herbert). *1.* August 12, 1925.

—— *and* GOSSE (Ellen, *Lady*) *from* ROBINSON (Agnes Mary Frances), *afterwards* Mme. James Darmesteter, *afterwards* Mme. Pierre Émile Duclaux. *1.* Undated.

—— *and* GOSSE (Ellen, *Lady*) *from* SCHWARTZ (Joost Marius Willem van der Poorten-), *pseud.* Maarten Maartens. *2.* June 26, 1911; May 19, 1913.
The letter of June 26, 1911, is a typewritten copy.

—— *and* GOSSE (Ellen, *Lady*) *from* SCHWARTZ (Joost Marius Willem van der Poorten-), *pseud.* Maarten Maartens *and* SCHWARTZ (Ada van der Poorten-). *1.* December 19, 1907.
Typewritten copy.

—— *and* GOSSE (Ellen, *Lady*) *from* TADEMA (Laura Theresa, *Lady* Alma-). *1.* [April 9? 1878].
Written in the blank space beneath the postscript of a letter from Sir Lawrence Alma-Tadema to Sir Edmund and Lady Gosse, dated April 8—9, 1878.

—— *and* GOSSE (Ellen, *Lady*) *from* TADEMA (*Sir* Lawrence Alma-). *4.* August 25, 1875—August 17, 1900.
Letter of April 8—9, 1878: written in the blank space beneath the postscript is a note from Laura Lady Alma-Tadema to Sir Edmund and Lady Gosse.

—— *and* GOSSE (Ellen, *Lady*) *from* THORNYCROFT (*Sir* William Hamo). *1* telegram. August 12, 1925.

—— *and* GOSSE (Ellen, *Lady*) *from* WRATISLAW (Theodore). *1.* August 11, 1925.

—— *and* SCHWARTZ (Joost Marius Willem van der Poorten-), *pseud.* Maarten Maartens, *from* WATTS (Walter Theodore), *afterwards* Watts-Dunton. *1.* June 10, 1895.

GOSSE (Elizabeth) *to* GOSSE (William). *1.* October 5, 1835.

GOSSE (Ellen, *Lady*). *2.* August 5, 1888; February 5, 1904.

—— *to* GODWIN (Fanny Bryant). *1.* [December, 1884?].
Draft, in the handwriting of Sir Edmund Gosse, of reply to Mrs. Godwin's letter to Lady Gosse, dated December 13, [1884]. Unsigned.

—— *from* BEERBOHM (*Sir* Max). *1.* March 19, 1929.

—— *from* BROWNING (Robert). *2.* November 5, 1884; May 18, 1886.

—— *from* BUCHANAN (*Sir* George William). *1.* Undated.

—— *from* GODWIN (Fanny Bryant). *1.* December 13, [1884].

—— *from* HALDANE (Richard Burdon), *1st Viscount Haldane of Cloan*. *2.* March 26, 1920; August 19, 1927.

—— *from* HARDY (Florence Emily) [Mrs. Thomas Hardy]. *2.* August 6, 1927; August 15, 1927.

—— *from* JAMES (Henry), *novelist*. *29.* April 7, 1886—December 7, 1913; *1* undated.
Only nine letters, dated December 14, 1902—September 27, 1911, are holograph; the rest are typewritten transcripts.

—— *from* MOORE (George Augustus). *2.* (July 4, 1896); December 25, [1913].

—— *from* NEWCOMBE (Bertha). *1.* March 8, (1900).

——*from* PANGE (Pauline de), *Comtesse Jean de Pange, née* de Broglie. *1*. [December] 15, 1921.
Dated incorrectly '15 Xᵉ 1921.'

——*from* RALEIGH (*Sir* Walter Alexander). *1*. September 16, (1889).

——*from* ROBINSON (Agnes Mary Frances), *afterwards* Mme. James Darmesteter, *afterwards* Mme. Pierre Émile Duclaux. *1*. January 8, 1879.

——*from* SABATIER (Paul). *1*. November 22, *1921*.

——*from* SPENCER (Charles Robert), *6th Earl Spencer*. *1*. March 3, 1922.

——*from* STEPHEN (*Sir* Herbert), *2nd Bart*. *1*. May 18, 1928.

——*from* SWINBURNE (Algernon Charles). *4*. January 10, [1877]—July 29, 1882.

——*from* SYMONS (Arthur). *1*. Undated.

——*from* TADEMA (*Sir* Lawrence Alma-). *1*. December 5. 1874.

——*from* WAGSTAFF (W. H.) [*for* the Royal Society of Literature of the United Kingdom]. *1*. May 23, 1928.

——*from* WATSON (Robinson). *2*. March 14, 1893; March 24, [1893].

—— from WOLSELEY (Garnet Joseph), *1st Viscount Wolseley*. *1* telegram. September 19, 1899.

——*from* WOLSELEY (Louisa), *Viscountess Wolseley*. *1*. June 5, 1892.

—— *see also* GOSSE (*Sir* Edmund William) *and* GOSSE (Ellen, *Lady*).

GOSSE (Gertrude Agnes) [Mrs. Philip Gosse]. *1*. September 18, [1919].

GOSSE (Hannah) *from* GOSSE (Philip Henry). *1*. December 29, 1844.
Duplicate copy only.

GOSSE (*Sir* James Hay). *1*. November 15, 1916.

GOSSE (Philip). *5*. February 22, 1906—January 17, 1928.

——*from* DOBSON (Alban Tabor Austin). *1*. March 19, 1934.

——*from* DOBSON (Henry Austin). *1*. (December 10, 1897).

——*from* GIDE (André Paul Guillaume). *5*. February 8, 1929—May 2, 1930.

——*from* GRAHAM (Robert Bontine Cunninghame). *1*. February 7, 1929.

D

—— *from* HONE (Joseph). *1*. September 23, 1936.

—— *from* JAMES (Henry), *nephew of novelist*. *1*. February 6, 1929.

—— *from* JAMES (Henry), *novelist*. *2*. October 14, 1896; November 26, 1899.
The letter dated October 14, 1896, is a typewritten transcript.

—— *from* KEEBLE (Lillah, *Lady*), *formerly* Mrs. Harley Granville-Barker, *née* McCarthy. *1*. November 5, 1932.

—— *from* KINGDON (Mona). *1*. November 7, 1932.

—— *from* MAGEE (William Kirkpatrick), *pseud.* John Eglington. *3*. September 25, 1936—October 2, 1936.

—— *from* MAURICE (*Sir* Frederick Barton). *1*. October 2, 1936.

—— *from* MOORE (George Augustus). *11*. January 6, 1922 —November 17, (1932).
Two letters, dated January 6, 1922, and November 1, 1932, are signed 'George Moore p.p. M. K.' [i.e. Mona Kingdon].

—— *from* MORGAN (Charles Langbridge). *1*. January 24, 1933.

—— *from* PALMER (E.) [*for* George Augustus Moore]. *1*. March 17, 1932.

—— *from* POTTER (George R.). *1*. March 30, 1930.

—— *from* PRICE (Lilian Nancy Bache), *afterwards* Mrs. Charles Raymond Maude. *1*. March 30, 1938.

—— *from* STREET (George Slythe). *1*. August 28, 1931.

—— *from* VAN DER POEL (A.). *1*. April 20, 1936.

GOSSE (Philip Henry) *to* CUMING (Hugh). *8*. January 23, 1845—January 27, 1846.
Duplicate copies only.

—— *to* DOUBLEDAY (Edward). *1*. July 16, 1845.

—— *to* GOSSE (Hannah). *1*. December 29, 1844.
Duplicate copy only.

—— *to* KINGSLEY (Charles). *12*. July 28, 1853—May 30, 1854; 1 undated.
The letter dated December 23 [25?], 1853, is incomplete.

—— *from* BLAIKIE (John Arthur). *1*. May 14, 1870.

—— *from* DARWIN (Charles Robert). *2*. April 27, [1857]; [June 2, 1863].

—— *from* KINGSLEY (Charles). *16*. January 4, 1854— May 4, 1858; 1 undated [incomplete].

—— *from* MÜLLER (Friedrich Max). *1*. October 18, [1869].

GOSSE (Sylvia). *2*. September 19, 1919; August 18, 1925.

GOSSE (Teresa). *1*. August 19, 1916.

—— *from* BARING (Maurice). *1*. September 7, 1929.

—— *from* JAMES (Henry), *novelist*. *2*. December 18, 1891;
July 17, 1906.
Typewritten transcripts.

GOSSE (Thomas) *to* GOSSE (William). *1*. March 16, 1835.

GOSSE (William) *from* GOSSE (Elizabeth). *1*. October 5, 1835.

—— *from* GOSSE (Thomas). *1*. March 16, 1835.

GOUGH (Hugh), *3rd Viscount Gough of Goojerat*. *1*. February 14,
1908.

GOURAUD (Henri). *1*. July 26, 1926.

GRAHAM (*Sir* Henry John Lowndes). *5*. February 5, 1904—
January 2, [1925].

—— *to* MARSH (*Sir* Edward Howard). *1*. February 7, 1902.

GRAHAM (Robert Bontine Cunninghame). *11*. [February ?]
12, 1917—March 26, 1928.

—— *to* GOSSE (Philip). *1*. February 7, 1929.

GRANARD (Bernard Arthur William Patrick Hastings Forbes,
8th Earl of), *see* FORBES (Bernard Arthur William Patrick
Hastings), *8th Earl of Granard*.

GRAND (Sarah) *pseud.* [*i.e.* Frances Elizabeth M'Fall], *see*
M'FALL (Frances Elizabeth) [Mrs. D. C. M'Fall],
pseud. Sarah Grand.

GRANVILLE-BARKER (Harley Granville). *2*. [October 12,
1915]; March 9, 1923.

GRANVILLE-BARKER (Lillah), *née* McCarthy [Mrs. Harley
Granville-Barker], *afterwards* Lady Keeble, *see* KEEBLE
(Lillah, *Lady*), *formerly* Mrs. Harley Granville-Barker,
née McCarthy.

GRAVES (Robert Ranke). *9*. March 23, 1917—[March,
1925?]; 2 undated.

GREENWOOD (Frederick). *3*. December 9, 1897—March 14,
1905.

GREG (Walter Wilson). *1*. January 16, 1924.

GREGH (Fernand). *1*. Undated.

GRENFELL (Ethel Anne Priscilla), *Baroness Desborough*. *8*.
May 15, 1908—January 1, 1925; 1 undated.

GRENFELL (Francis Wallace), *1st Baron Grenfell of Kilvey*. *2*.
April 13, 1908; 1 undated.

—— *to* SANDERSON [Thomas Henry Sanderson, *1st Baron
Sanderson of Armthorpe?*]. *1*. December 2, 1916.

GRENFELL (William Henry), *1st Baron Desborough of Taplow*. *2*. September 24, 1919; May 18, 1920.

GRIERSON (*Sir* Herbert John Clifford). *5*. August 26, 1915— March 24, 1922; 1 undated.

GRISEBACH (Eduard). *2*. February 15, 1874; March 20, 1874.

GROSVENOR (Hugh Lupus), *1st Duke of Westminster, see* SCOTLAND (D.) [*for* Hugh Lupus Grosvenor, *1st Duke of Westminster*].

GROVE (*Mrs.* Lilly), *afterwards* Lady Frazer, *see* FRAZER (Lilly, *Lady*), *formerly* Mrs. Grove.

GUEDALLA (Philip). *1*. August 7, 1925.

GUINEY (Grace). *1*. July 11, 1923.

GUINEY (Louise Imogen). *1*. June 10, [1908].

—— *to* ROSS (A. G.). *1*. May 8, 1919.

GULLICK (Norman). *1*. January 30, 1921.

GULLY (William Court), *1st Viscount Selby*. *1*. December 15, 1908.

GURNEY (Edmund). *1*. February 10, 1884.

GUTHRIE (Thomas Anstey), *pseud.* F. Anstey. *6*. October 24, 1887—January 1, 1925.

H

HADLEY (Arthur Twining). *1*. August 31, 1914.

HAEHNEL (Julius). *1*. February 28, 1882.

—— *to* WOOLNER (Thomas). *2*. December 20, 1881; January 5, 1882.
Letter of January 5, 1882: enclosed in a letter from Thomas Woolner to Sir Edmund Gosse, dated [February? 1882].

HAGGARD (*Sir* Henry Rider). *4*. December 29, 1886— January 1, 1925.

—— *to* ROSS (A.G.). *1*. December 19, 1918.

HAIG (Douglas), *1st Earl Haig, to* SANDERSON (Thomas Henry), *1st Baron Sanderson of Armthorpe*. *1*. June 27, 1919.
Enclosed in a letter from Lord Sanderson to Sir Edmund Gosse, dated June 30, 1919.

HALDANE (Elizabeth Sanderson). *11*. December 25, 1913— April 8, 1925; 1 undated.

HALDANE (Mary Elizabeth) [Mrs. Robert Haldane]. *2*. November 21, 1915; May 26, 1923.

HALDANE (Richard Burdon), *1st Viscount Haldane of Cloan*. *605*. July 17, 1903—March 8, 1928.

—— *to* GOSSE (Ellen, *Lady*). *2.* March 26, 1920; August 19, 1927.

—— *to* LUND (Troels Frederik). *1.* September 15, 1914.
A copy, in Sir Edmund Gosse's hand.

——*from* BALSILLIE (David). *1.* May 8, 1920.

——*from* BERESFORD (Charles William De la Poer), *1st Baron Beresford of Metemmeh and Curraghmore. 1.* July 8, 1917.

——*from* BIGGE (*Sir* Lewis Amherst Selby-), *1st Bart. 1.* August 21, 1917.

——*from* DAWSON (Geoffrey). *1.* December 13, 1918.

——*from* HOLLAND (Sydney George), *2nd Viscount Knutsford of Knutsford. 1.* September 10, [1917].

——*from* LISTER (Thomas), *4th Baron Ribblesdale of Gisburne Park. 1.* Undated.

——*from* LOWELL (Abbott Lawrence). *1.* September 8, 1914.

——*from* MALCOLM (*Sir* Ian Zachary). *1.* August 8, [1918].

——*from* MITFORD (Algernon Bertram Freeman-), *1st Baron Redesdale of Redesdale. 1.* August 10, 1916.

——*from* MORLEY (John), *1st Viscount Morley of Blackburn. 1.* December 27, 1916.

——*from* PONSONBY (Frederick Edward Grey), *1st Baron Sysonby of Wonersh. 1.* November 30, 1916.

HALE (Edward Everett). *1.* December 6, 1884.

—— *to* STOCKTON [Francis Richard Stockton?]. *1.* December 12, 1884.

HALIBURTON (Mariana Emily), *Baroness Haliburton. 1.* (December) 22, (1913).

HALIFAX (Charles Lindley Wood, *2nd Viscount*), *see* WOOD (Charles Lindley), *2nd Viscount Halifax.*

HALIFAX (Edward Frederick Lindley Wood, *1st Earl of*), *see* WOOD (Edward Frederick Lindley), *1st Earl of Halifax.*

HALLSTRÖM (Per August Leonard). *1.* April 17, 1911.

HAMILTON (Clayton). *1.* August 4, 1910.

HAMILTON (Gavin George), *2nd Baron Hamilton of Dalzell. 2.* August 22, 1909; November 23, 1914.

HANNAH (R.). *1.* April 25, 1878.

HANWORTH (Ernest Murray Pollock, *1st Viscount*), *see* POLLOCK (Ernest Murray), *1st Viscount Hanworth of Hanworth.*

HAPGOOD (Norman). *1.* June 22, 1919.

HARCOURT (Lewis), *1st Viscount Harcourt of Stanton Harcourt.* *9.* March 19, 1908—December 6, 1918; 1 undated.
Letter of November 23, 1916: enclosed in a letter [*c.* November 25, 1916] from Sir William Hamo Thornycroft to Sir Edmund Gosse.

—— *from* GOSSE (*Sir* Edmund William). *1.* [March 24, 1908].
Rough draft, unsigned.

HARDY (Florence Emily) [Mrs. Thomas Hardy]. *17.* June 10, 1922—February 21, 1928.
To a letter dated June 26, 1924, is added a postscript in the handwriting of Thomas Hardy.

—— *to* GOSSE (Ellen, *Lady*). *2.* August 6, 1927; August 15, 1927.

HARDY (Thomas). *80.* May 19, 1886—November 20, 1927; 1 undated. *Also 2* telegrams. November 24, 1902; June 22, 1910.
The letter dated July 7, 1906, is a copy, in the handwriting of Sir Edmund Gosse.

HARLAND (Aline) [Mrs. Henry Harland]. *2.* December 30, 1905; March 1, [1907].

—— *from* BIGELOW (Henry). *1.* [*c.* 1898].

HARLAND (Henry) *from* MAKOWER (Stanley). *1.* June 7, 1905.

HARMSWORTH (Alfred Charles William), *1st Viscount Northcliffe of St. Peter. 10.* October 12, 1906—December 14, 1911.

HARPER & BROTHERS, *publishers, New York, see* ALDEN (Henry Mills) [*for* Harper & Brothers, *publishers, New York*].

HARPER (   ) *from* CURTIS (George William). *1.* December 29, 1884.

HARRIS (George Robert Canning), *4th Baron Harris of Seringapatam and Mysore. 2.* July 10, 1919; 1 undated.

HARRIS (James Edward), *5th Earl of Malmesbury. 3.* April 6, 1906—November 23, 1922.

HARRISON (Frederic). *56.* May 4, 1896—December 19, 1922.

—— *to* LANE (John). *1.* March 20, 1919.

—— *to* MILNES (Robert Offley Ashburton Crewe-), *1st Marquis of Crewe. 1.* September 21, 1919.
Typewritten transcript.

HARRISON (Jane Ellen). *1.* October 24, 1888.

HAVET (Ernest). *2.* July 12, 1878; September 23, 1878.

HAY (John). *3.* March 8, 1897—September 12, 1898.

HAYES (Alfred). *1.* May 4, 1893.

HEATHCOTE-DRUMMOND-WILLOUGHBY (Gilbert), *2nd Earl of Ancaster.* *1.* November 11, 1911.

HEDGCOCK (Frank Arthur). *1.* July 22, 1909.

HEGEL (Frederik). *1.* November 8, 1908.

HEINEMANN (William). *2.* January 18, 1906; September 18, 1919.

—— *from* HICHENS (Robert Smythe). *1.* August 5, 1909.
Typewritten transcript.

—— *from* PALACIO VALDÉS (Armando). *1.* July 14, 1894.

HELY-HUTCHINSON (Richard Walter John), *6th Earl of Donoughmore.* *6.* June 14, 1912—September 28, 1926.

HENLEY (William Ernest). *5.* [November 19, 1888]—February 11, 1892.

HENNIKER (*Mrs.* Arthur), *novelist [i.e.* Florence Ellen Hungerford Henniker-Major], *see* HENNIKER-MAJOR (Florence Ellen Hungerford) [Mrs. Arthur Henry Henniker-Major].

HENNIKER-MAJOR (Florence Ellen Hungerford) [Mrs. Arthur Henry Henniker-Major]. *1.* September 21, [1919].

HENRY (Fernand). *5.* February 6, 1903—December 12, 1913.

HERBERT (Edward James), *3rd Earl of Powis,* *1.* December 7, 1883.

HERBERT (George Robert Charles), *13th Earl of Pembroke.* *3.* June 30, 1888—July 20, 1892.

HEREDIA (José Maria de). *2.* June 9, 1894; (1905).

—— *to* DAVRAY (Henry D.). *1.* (February 5, 1904).

HEREFORD (Robert Devereux, *16th Viscount*), *see* DEVEREUX (Robert), *16th Viscount Hereford.*

HERKOMER (*Sir* Hubert von). *10.* June 11, 1882—March 19, 1885; 1 undated.

HERSCHELL (Richard Farrer), *2nd Baron Herschell of Durham.* *1.* June 27, 1913.

—— *see also* COLEBROOKE (Edward Arthur), *1st Baron Colebrooke of Stebunheath, and* HERSCHELL (Richard Farrer), *2nd Baron Herschell of Durham.*

HERVEY (*Lord* Arthur Charles), *Bishop of Bath and Wells.* *1.* December 5, 1883.

HERZOG (Émile Salomon Wilhelm), *pseud.* André Maurois. *1.* September 7, 1923.

HEWLETT (Hilda Beatrice) [Mrs. Maurice Henry Hewlett].
1. June 15, 1923.

HEWLETT (Maurice Henry). *71*. April 13, 1900—November
2, 1920; 6 undated.

—— *to* Ross (A.G.). *1*. December 18, 1918.

HIBBEN (John Grier). *1*. September 15, 1914.

HICHENS (Robert Smythe). *2*. August 8, 1909; August 10,
1909.

—— *to* HEINEMANN (William). *1*. August 5, 1909.
Typewritten transcript.

HIGGINSON (Ella). *1*. March 31, 1903.

HILL (Rowland Richard Clegg-), *4th Viscount Hill of
Hawkstone and Hardwicke*. *2*. July 17, 1911; July 19, 1911.

HILLINGDON (Arthur Robert Mills, *3rd Baron*), *see* MILLS
(Arthur Robert), *3rd Baron Hillingdon*.

HOBBES (John Oliver) *pseud*. [*i.e.* Pearl Mary Teresa Craigie],
see CRAIGIE (Pearl Mary Teresa) [Mrs. Reginald
Walpole Craigie], *pseud*. John Oliver Hobbes.

HODGKIN (Wilfred H.). *2*. June 24, 1873; August 3, 1873.

HOLLAND (*Mrs.* E.). *1*. February 6, 1884.

HOLLAND (Henry Thurstan), *1st Viscount Knutsford of Knutsford*. *11*. April 29, [1904]—August 3, 1913.

HOLLAND (Sydney George), *2nd Viscount Knutsford of Knutsford*. *6*. January 14, 1908—October 25, 1917; 1
undated.

—— *to* HALDANE (Richard Burdon), *1st Viscount Haldane of
Cloan*. *1*. September 10, [1917].

—— *from* LYGON (William), *7th Earl Beauchamp*. *1*. May 13,
1919.

HOLMAN-HUNT (William). *1*. February 9, 1899.

HOLMES (Oliver Wendell). *10*. September 7, 1884—
November 27, 1890.

HOLMES (Timothy). *1*. January 14, 1884.

HOME (*Lady* Alexandra Margaret Elizabeth Douglas-),
née Spencer, *see* SPENCER (*Lady* Alexandra Margaret
Elizabeth), *afterwards* Douglas-Home.

HOME (Cecil) *pseud*. [*i.e.* Julia Augusta Webster], *see* WEBSTER
(Julia Augusta) [Mrs. Thomas Webster], *pseud*. Cecil
Home.

HONE (Joseph) *to* GOSSE (Philip). *1*. September 23, 1936.

HOPWOOD (Francis John Stephens), *1st Baron Southborough of
Southborough*. *1*. September 21, 1921.

HORNBY (Charles Harry St. John). *1.* March 26, 1922.

HORNE (Richard Henry) [*also known as* Richard Hengist Horne]. *44.* December 30, 1876—May 11, 1882.

——*from* LUCY (*Sir* Henry William). *1.* June 28, 1878.

HORNER (Frances, *Lady*). *1* telegram. September 22, 1919.

—— *to* KELLY (James Fitzmaurice-). *1.* May 20, [1919].

HOSKEN (J.D.). *3.* April 20, 1900—February 3, 1909.

HOUGHTON (A. V.) [*for* the English Association]. *2.* February 21, 1921; February 24, 1921.

HOUGHTON (Richard Monckton Milnes, *1st Baron*), *see* MILNES (Richard Monckton), *1st Baron Houghton of Great Houghton.*

HOUSMAN (Alfred Edward). *2.* January 19, 1911; December 11, 1913.

HOWARD (George James), *9th Earl of Carlisle.* *3.* Undated.

HOWARD (Henry Newman). *4.* January 4, 1901—May 6, 1923.

HOWARD DE WALDEN (Thomas Evelyn Scott-Ellis, *8th Baron*), *see* ELLIS (Thomas Evelyn Scott-), *8th Baron Howard de Walden.*

HOWARTH (Arthur H.). *1.* May 4, 1927.

HOWELLS (William Dean). *4.* June 15, 1883—January 25, 1885.

——*from* JAMES (Henry), *novelist.* *1.* July 1, [1894].
Enclosed in James's letter to Sir Edmund Gosse, dated the same day.

—— *see also* BOOTH (Edwin) *to* HOWELLS [William Dean Howells ?]

HOYT (Maud Buckingham). *2.* [November 27, 1925]; 1 undated.

HSU (Tsemoo). *1.* August 12, 1922.

HUDSON (Frederic) *from* GOSSE (*Sir* Edmund William). *2.* November 2, 1895; October 8, 1896.

HUDSON (*Sir* Robert Arundell) [*for* the Joint War Committee of the British Red Cross Society and the Order of St. John of Jerusalem in England]. *1.* January 18, 1918.

HUGGINS (*Sir* William). *1.* June 23, 1897.

HUGHES (Thomas). *2.* January 5, 1882; February 5, 1882.

HUME (Fergus). *1.* February 28, 1924.

HUME (Martin Andrew Sharp). *1.* January 20, 1905.

HUNGARIAN ACADEMY OF SCIENCES [*Magyar Tudományos Akadémia*], *see* SZILY VON NAGYSZIGETH (Coloman) [*for* the Hungarian Academy of Sciences].

HUNT (Alfred William). *1*. Undated.
HUNT (William). *16*. November 4, 1897—[April 18], 1927.
Letter dated July 2, 1901: enclosed is a letter from Sir Charles Harding
Firth to William Hunt, dated June 30, 1901.
—— *to* Ross (A. G.). *1*. December 18, 1918.
—— *from* FIRTH (*Sir* Charles Harding). *1*. June 30, 1901.
Enclosed in a letter from William Hunt to Sir Edmund Gosse, dated
July 2, 1901.
HUTTON (Richard Holt). *5*. December 12, 1892—March 11,
1893.
—— *from* GOSSE (*Sir* Edmund William). *1*. March 10, 1893.
Typewritten, including signature. Copy?
HUXLEY (Thomas Henry). *2*. October 22, 1886; March 22,
1889.
HYDE (Douglas). *1*. May 12, 1896.

I

IBSEN (Henrik). *3*. January 27, 1891—August 30, 1899.
Also 1 telegram. January 30, 1891.
—— *from* GOSSE (*Sir* Edmund William). *1*. March 17, 1898.
Draft.
IBSEN (Sigurd). *1*. January 16, 1908.
ILBERT (*Sir* Courtenay Peregrine). *3*. May 6, 1900—
July 24, 1912.
—— *from* BALFOUR (Arthur James), *1st Earl of Balfour*. *1*.
June 22, 1918.
ILCHESTER (Giles Stephen Holland Fox-Strangways, *6th Earl
of*), *see* FOX-STRANGWAYS (Giles Stephen Holland), *6th
Earl of Ilchester*.
ILCHESTER (Helen Mary Theresa Fox-Strangways, *Countess
of*), *see* FOX-STRANGWAYS (Helen Mary Theresa), *Countess of Ilchester*.
INCHBOLD (John William). *1*. August 3, 1883.
INGE (William Ralph), *Dean of St. Paul's*. *4*. September 19,
[1919]—[November, 1925]; 1 undated.
INGELOW (Jean). *4*. December 15, 1873—[August 4, 1885];
1 undated.
IRELAND (Alexander). *1*. January 7, 1892.
IRVING (*Sir* Henry). *3* telegrams. August 10, 1891 [2];
August 12, 1891.
IRVING (Henry Brodribb). *1*. April 25, 1901.
ISLINGTON (John Poynder Dickson-Poynder, *1st Baron*), *see*
DICKSON-POYNDER (John Poynder), *1st Baron Islington of
Islington*.

J

JACKSON (Henry). *1.* July 7, 1897.

JAGO (James Baynes). *1.* September 21, 1919.

JAMES (Alice H.) [Mrs. William James]. *3.* February 11, 1916—August 2, 1916.

JAMES (Henry), *1st Baron James of Hereford.* *2.* August 28, 1907; January 5, 1911.

JAMES (Henry), *nephew of novelist.* *1.* May 21, 1919.

—— *to* GOSSE (Philip). *1.* February 6, 1929.

—— *to* LUBBOCK (Percy). *1.* May 20, 1919.
Carbon copy, unsigned.

JAMES (Henry), *novelist.* *249.* August 2, [1882]—July 9, 1915. *Also 5* telegrams. January 4, 1891—September 26, 1911.
Enclosed in the letter of July 1, 1894, is one to William Dean Howells, dated the same day.

—— *to* GOSSE (*Sir* Edmund William) *and* BESANT (*Sir* Walter). *1.* July 12, [1888].

—— *to* GOSSE (*Sir* Edmund William) *and* GOSSE (Ellen, *Lady*). *2.* October 14, 1907; [December 29, 1908].

—— *to* GOSSE (Ellen, *Lady*). *29.* April 7, 1886—December 7, 1913; 1 undated.
Only nine letters, dated December 14, 1902—September 27, 1911, are holograph; the rest are typewritten transcripts.

—— *to* GOSSE (Philip). *2.* October 14, 1896; November 26, 1899.
The letter dated October 14, 1896, is a typewritten transcript.

—— *to* GOSSE (Teresa). *2.* December 18, 1891; July 17, 1906.
Typewritten transcripts.

—— *to* HOWELLS (William Dean). *1.* July 1, [1894].
Enclosed in James's letter to Sir Edmund Gosse, dated the same day.

—— *see also* COLVIN (*Sir* Sidney) *to* [JAMES (Henry), *novelist?*].

JAMES (William). *1.* June 14, 1910.

JEBB (*Sir* Richard Claverhouse). *14.* April 7, 1884—July 1, 1905; 1 undated.

JERSEY (Margaret Elizabeth Child-Villiers, *Countess of*), *see* VILLIERS (Margaret Elizabeth Child-), *Countess of Jersey.*

JESPERSEN (Jens Otto Harry). *1.* July 27, 1918.

JESSOPP (Augustus). *9.* November 5, 1892—December 22, 1910.

JEUNE (John Frederic Symons-). *1.* September 21, 1919.

JOHN (*Sir* William Goscombe). *7.* February 5, 1899—August 12, 1925.

JOHNSON (Lionel Pigot). *8*. October 31, 1892—March 20, 1899.

JOHNSTON (*Sir* Harry Hamilton). *8*. July 18, 1894—April 12, 1907; 1 undated.

—— *to* Ross (A. G.). *1*. May 14, 1919.

JONES (G. M. E.). *1*. Undated.

JONES (Henry Arthur) *from* GOSSE (*Sir* Edmund William). *11*. October 11, 1889—September 16, 1925.

JONES (Henry Festing). *4*. December 24, 1912—December 14, 1918.

JONES (Herbert), *see* JONES (Loe) *and* JONES (Herbert).

JONES (Loe) *and* JONES (Herbert) *to* GOSSE *(Sir* Edmund William) *and* GOSSE (Ellen, *Lady*). *1*. August 12, 1925.

JONES (Mary). *1*. October 13, 1918.

JONES (William Garmon) [*for* the University of Liverpool]. *1*. May 2, 1919.

JUHELLÉ (Albert). *1*. June 11, 1898.

JUSSERAND (Jean Adrien Antoine Jules). *18*. February 8, 1888—December 8, 1925; 1 undated.

JUST (H. W.) [*for* Edward Henry Stanley, *15th Earl of Derby*]. *1*. March 12, 1884.

K

KANN (Edouard). *1*. December 26, 1916.

KEEBLE (Lillah, *Lady*), *formerly* Mrs. Harley Granville-Barker, *née* McCarthy, *to* GOSSE (Philip). *1*. November 5, 1932.

KELLY (James Fitzmaurice-). *52*. August 1, 1895—August 13, 1920.

—— *to* Ross (A. G.). *1*. December 20, 1918.

—— *from* BILDT (Carl Nils Daniel), *Baron de Bildt*. *1*. May 12, 1919.

—— *from* BULLER (*Lady* Audrey Jane Charlotte). *1*. May 9, 1919.

—— *from* DOBSON (Henry Austin). *1*. December 21, 1918.

—— *from* HORNER (Frances, *Lady*). *1*. May 20, [1919].

—— *from* MILNES (Robert Offley Ashburton Crewe-), *1st Marquis of Crewe*. *1*. December 19, 1918.

—— *from* WEDMORE (*Sir* Frederick). *1*. November 11, [1920].
Written on his behalf in an unidentified hand.

—— *see also* MORLEY (John), *1st Viscount Morley of Blackburn to* [KELLY (James Fitzmaurice-) ?].

KEMP (Francis H. N. C.). *1.* October 22, 1914.

KEMSLEY (James Gomer Berry, *1st Viscount*), *see* BERRY (James Gomer), *1st Viscount Kemsley of Dropmore*.

KER (William Paton). *15.* February 21, 1899—June 6, 1920.

KEY (Ellen Karolina Sofia). *2.* August 9, 1902; October 17, 1919.

KEYES (Roger John Brownlow), *1st Baron Keyes of Zeebrugge and of Dover. 1.* December 10, 1925.

KEYNES (Geoffrey Langdon). *3.* April 20, 1913—April 22, 1913.

KIDD (Benjamin). *1.* November 8, 1907.

KILBRACKEN (John Arthur Godley, *1st Baron*), *see* GODLEY (John Arthur), *1st Baron Kilbracken of Killegar*.

KINGDON (Mona) *to* GOSSE (Philip). *1.* November 7, 1932.

KING-NOEL (Ralph Gordon Noel), *afterwards* Milbanke, *2nd Earl of Lovelace. 1.* January 17, 1906.

KINGSLEY (Charles) *to* GOSSE (Philip Henry). *16.* January 4, 1854—May 4, 1858; 1 undated [incomplete].

—— *from* GOSSE (Philip Henry). *12.* July 28, 1853—May 30, 1854; 1 undated.

The letter dated December 23 [25?], 1853, is incomplete.

KINNAIRD (Arthur Fitzgerald), *11th Baron Kinnaird of Inchture. 1.* March 18, 1909.

KINNEAR (Alexander Smith), *1st Baron Kinnear of Spurness. 1.* June 13, 1911.

KIPLING (Rudyard). *1.* Undated.

KIRKPATRICK (Alexander Francis), *Dean of Ely. 2.* July 6, 1913; July 8, 1913.

KLEINE (F. Smit). *3.* June 14, 1911—July 24, 1911.

KLINCKOWSTRÖM (Axel Alexander Camille Rudolf Emanuel). *1.* February 3, 1923.

KNIGHT (Joseph). *1.* December 17, 1873.

KNUTSFORD (Henry Thurstan Holland, *1st Viscount*), *see* HOLLAND (Henry Thurstan), *1st Viscount Knutsford of Knutsford*.

KNUTSFORD (Sydney George Holland, *2nd Viscount*), *see* HOLLAND (Sydney George), *2nd Viscount Knutsford of Knutsford*.

KOEBERLÉ (Elsa). *1.* [May 27, 1913].

KOSZUL (André H.). *2.* December 4, 1921; February 4, 1922.

L

LAMBART (Frederick Rudolph), *10th Earl of Cavan.* *6.* December 23, 1926; December 25, 1926; 4 undated.
LAMBERT (Édouard). *1.* November 18, 1917.
LANE (John) *from* AUSTIN (Alfred). *1.* December 2, 1909.
—— *from* BALESTIER (Charles Wolcott). *1.* October 21, 1890.
—— *from* COLVIN (*Sir* Sidney). *1.* November 24, 1900.
—— *from* GARNETT (Richard). *1.* March 16, 1895.
—— *from* HARRISON (Frederic). *1.* March 20, 1919.
—— *from* MONKHOUSE (William Cosmo). *1.* August 21, 1890.
LANG (Andrew). *204.* [November 26, 1877]—November 27, [1911]; 19 undated.
—— *to* POLLOCK [Walter Herries Pollock ?] *1.* Undated.
—— *from* ROBERTS (A. Llewelyn). *1.* January 4, 1890.
LANG (Cosmo Gordon), *Archbishop, first, of York; afterwards, of Canterbury.* *3.* November 30, 1920—January 24, 1925.
—— *see also* BOOKER (Robert A. D.) [*for* Cosmo Gordon Lang, *Archbishop of York*].
LANG (Leonora Blanche) [Mrs. Andrew Lang]. *1.* [July 26, 1912].
LANGE (Julius Henrik). *2.* January 30, 1874; May 15, 1874.
LANKESTER (*Sir* Edwin Ray). *33.* [August 6, 1898]—November 18, [1927]; 6 undated.
Letter dated February 22, [1917]: enclosed is a letter from the Marquis of Crewe to Sir Edwin Lankester, dated February 21, 1917.
—— *from* MILNES (Robert Offley Ashburton Crewe-), *1st Marquis of Crewe.* *1.* February 21, 1917.
Enclosed in a letter from Sir Edwin Lankester to Sir Edmund Gosse, dated February 22, [1917].
LANSDOWNE (Henry Charles Keith Petty Fitzmaurice, *5th Marquis of*), *see* FITZMAURICE (Henry Charles Keith Petty), *5th Marquis of Lansdowne.*
LANSON (Gustave). *2.* September 29, 1918; June 22, 1922.
LAPIE (P.) [*for* the University of Paris]. *1.* November 2, 1925.
LAPSLEY (Gaillard Thomas) *from* WHARTON (Edith Newbold) [Mrs. Edward Wharton]. *1.* February 7, 1911.
LARBAUD (Valery). *1.* March 1, 1918.

LATHBURY (Daniel Conner). *1.* November 6, 1896.

LAU-BROWN (Astrid). *1.* August 18, 1925.

LAWLESS (Emily). *2.* April 2, 1894; February 3, 1908.

LEA (Henry Charles). *1.* September 10, 1890.

LEAF (Walter H.). *2.* March 30, 1914; March 2, 1923.

LECKY (William Edward Hartpole). *1.* January 21, 1898.

LECONFIELD (Charles Henry Wyndham, *3rd Baron*), *see*
WYNDHAM (Charles Henry), *3rd Baron Leconfield of
Leconfield.*

LECONFIELD (Constance Evelyn Wyndham, *Baroness*), *see*
WYNDHAM (Constance Evelyn), *Baroness Leconfield.*

LEE (*Sir* Sidney). *1.* April 16, 1913.

LEE (Vernon) *pseud.* [*i.e.* Violet Paget], *see* PAGET (Violet),
pseud. Vernon Lee.

LEFFLER (Anne Charlotte Gustava), *afterwards* fru G. E.
Edgren, *afterwards* Duchèssa di Cajanello. *1.* May 22,
1884.

LE GALLIENNE (Richard). *23.* December 21, 1891—May 3,
1894.

LEGGE (William Heneage), *6th Earl of Dartmouth.* *1.*
February 26, 1909.

LEGH (Evelyn Caroline), *Baroness Newton.* *9.* January 11,
1916—August 22, 1925.

LEGH (Thomas Wodehouse), *2nd Baron Newton of Newton-in-
Makerfield.* *19.* October 12, 1913—August 22, 1925.

LEGOUIS (Émile). *12.* November 9, 1913—December 10,
1925.

LEIGHTON (Frederic), *1st Baron Leighton of Stretton.* *4.*
October 17, 1883; 3 undated.

LEITH (Alicia A.). *1.* February 20, [1899 ?].

LEITH (Mary Charlotte Julia) [Mrs. Disney Leith] *to* WISE
(Thomas James). *1.* August 3, 1915.

LEMON (Arthur) *and* OSBORNE (Charles C.). *1.* March 29,
1909.

—— *and* OSBORNE (Charles C.) *to* MEIKLEJOHN (*Sir* Roderick
Sinclair). *1.* April 5, 1909.
Typewritten copy, unsigned. Enclosed in a letter dated the same day
from Charles C. Osborne to Sir Edmund Gosse.

LEMPERLY (Paul) *to* WISE (Thomas James). *1.* July 4, 1909.

LEVESON-GOWER (*Sir* George Granville). *1.* February 13,
1902.

LEVINE (Isaac). *1.* May 27, 1911.

LEWIS (Elisabeth, *Lady*). *1*. March 17, [1884?].

LEYDEN, *Maatschappij der Nederlandsche Letterkunde te Leiden*, see FRANTZEN (J. J. A. A.) [*for* the *Maatschappij der Nederlandsche Letterkunde te Leiden*].

LEYRET (Henry). *1*. September 29, 1915.

LIE (Jonas Lauritz Idemil). *3*. December 30, 1875—June 7, 1877.

LIGHTFOOT (Joseph Barber), *Bishop of Durham*. *2*. December 3, 1883; October 14, 1884.

LINCOLNSHIRE (Charles Robert Wynn-Carrington, *1st Marquis of*), see CARRINGTON (Charles Robert Wynn-), *1st Marquis of Lincolnshire*.

LINDLEY (*Sir* Francis Oswald). *1*. March 30, 1928.
Enclosed is a typewritten copy of a letter from Sir Francis Lindley to Dr. Sæland, *Rektor* of Oslo University, dated the same day.

—— *to* SÆLAND (S.). *1*. March 30, 1928.
Typewritten copy. Enclosed in a letter bearing the same date from Sir Francis Lindley to Sir Edmund Gosse.

LINDSAY (David Alexander Edward), *27th Earl of Crawford and 10th Earl of Balcarres*. *26*. January 23, 1905—July 22, 1927.

LINDSAY (Jack). *9*. October 24, 1927—February 6, 1928; 2 undated.

LISTER (Thomas), *4th Baron Ribblesdale of Gisburne Park*. *23*. July 18, 1907—July 30, 1919; 3 undated.
Letter dated May 26, [1909]: enclosed is a card from G. H. Powell, bookseller, to Lord Ribblesdale, dated May 20, 1909.

—— *to* HALDANE (Richard Burdon), *1st Viscount Haldane of Cloan*. *1*. Undated.

—— *from* POWELL (George Herbert). *1*. May 20, 1909.
Enclosed in a letter from Lord Ribblesdale to Sir Edmund Gosse, dated May 26, [1909].

LIVERPOOL, *University*, see JONES (William Garmon) [*for* the University of Liverpool].

LIVINGSTONE (Millicent Julia) [Mrs. Richard John Livingstone]. *1*. Undated.

LOCKE (J. W. F.). *1*. November 9, 1920.

LOCKER (Frederick), *afterwards* Locker-Lampson. *7*. [April 26, 1877]—August 26, 1893; 1 undated.

LODER (Gerald Walter Erskine). *2*. January 2, 1917; January 5, 1917.

LODGE (Henry Cabot). *1*. December 21, 1884.

LOEB (James). *3*. May 30, 1924; December 17, 1926; 1 undated.

LÖKKE (Jakob Olaus). *14.* October 14, 1872—November 15, 1874.

LOFTIE (William John). *1.* October 14, 1884.

LONDON, *University, University College, see* SETON (Walter W.) [*for* University College, London].

LONDONDERRY (Charles Stewart Henry Vane-Tempest-Stewart, *7th Marquis of*), *see* VANE-TEMPEST-STEWART (Charles Stewart Henry), *7th Marquis of Londonderry.*

LONDONDERRY (Charles Stewart Vane-Tempest-Stewart, *6th Marquis of*), *see* VANE-TEMPEST-STEWART (Charles Stewart), *6th Marquis of Londonderry.*

LONDONDERRY (Edith Helen Vane-Tempest-Stewart, *Marchioness of*), *see* VANE-TEMPEST-STEWART (Edith Helen), *Marchioness of Londonderry.*

LONDONDERRY (Theresa Susey Helen Vane-Tempest-Stewart, *Marchioness of*), *see* VANE-TEMPEST-STEWART (Theresa Susey Helen), *Marchioness of Londonderry.*

LONG (Walter Hume), *1st Viscount Long of Wraxall.* *1.* March 30, 1914.

LOREBURN (Robert Threshie Reid, *1st Earl*), *see* REID (Robert Threshie), *1st Earl Loreburn.*

LOVELACE (Ralph Gordon Noel Milbanke, *2nd Earl of*), *see* KING-NOEL (Ralph Gordon Noel), *afterwards* Milbanke, *2nd Earl of Lovelace.*

LOVENJOUL (Charles de), *see* SPOELBERCH DE LOVENJOUL (Alfred Charles Joseph de), *Vicomte.*

LOW (Seth). *1.* September 10, 1914.

LOW (*Sir* Sidney James Mark). *21.* October 30, 1897—January 15, 1920.

LOWELL (Abbott Lawrence) *to* HALDANE (Richard Burdon), *1st Viscount Haldane of Cloan.* *1.* September 8, 1914.

LOWELL (James Russell). *6.* July 26, 1883—May 10, 1885; 1 undated.

LOWTHER (James William), *1st Viscount Ullswater of Campsea Ashe.* *2.* May 26, 1919; August 13, 1925.

LUBBOCK (John), *1st Baron Avebury of Avebury.* *1.* November 21, 1902.

LUBBOCK (Percy). *15.* April 11, 1913—January 12, 1925; 1 undated.

—— *from* JAMES (Henry), *nephew of novelist*. *1*. May 20, 1919.
Carbon copy, unsigned.

LUCAN (George Bingham, *4th Earl of*), *see* BINGHAM (George),
4th Earl of Lucan.

LUCAS (Edward Verrall). *3*. November 22, 1921—February
4, 1925.

LUCAS (St. John Welles). *1*. Undated.

LUCY (Alfred Fabre). *1*. September 21, [1919].

LUCY (*Sir* Henry William). *1*. October 20, 1914.

—— *to* HORNE (Richard Henry) [*also known as* Richard
Hengist Horne]. *1*. June 28, 1878.

LUND (Troels Frederik). *8*. September 4, 1900—November
19, 1918.

—— *from* HALDANE (Richard Burdon), *1st Viscount Haldane
of Cloan*. *1*. September 15, 1914.
A copy, in Sir Edmund Gosse's hand.

LYGON (Henry). *1*. September 19, 1916.

LYGON (Lettice Mary Elizabeth), *Countess Beauchamp*, *see*
LYGON (William), *7th Earl Beauchamp*, *and* LYGON
(Lettice Mary Elizabeth), *Countess Beauchamp*.

LYGON (William), *7th Earl Beauchamp*. *7*. May 3, 1904—
May 27, 1915.

—— *to* HOLLAND (Sydney George), *2nd Viscount Knutsford of
Knutsford*. *1*. May 13, 1919.

—— *and* LYGON (Lettice Mary Elizabeth), *Countess Beauchamp*. *1*. August 13, 1925.

LYNCH (Hannah). *3*. August 17, 1903—December 23, 1903.

LYND (Robert). *3*. June 2, 1923—October 24, 1927.

LYTTELTON (Alfred). *1*. June 13, 1906.

LYTTELTON (*Sir* Neville Gerald). *1*. November 6, 1921.

LYTTON (Edith Bulwer-), *Countess of Lytton*. *1*. July 6, 1926.
Also 1 telegram. August 13, 1925.

LYTTON (Edward Robert Bulwer-), *1st Earl of Lytton*. *11*.
July 11, 1883—March 1, 1891.

LYTTON (Judith Anne Dorothea Blunt-), *afterwards* Milbanke,
Baroness Wentworth. *1*. January 16, 1914.

LYTTON (Victor Alexander George Robert Bulwer-), *2nd Earl
of Lytton*. *29*. May 15, 1899—December 31, 1918.

—— *from* WYNDHAM (Charles Henry), *3rd Baron Leconfield of
Leconfield*. *1*. November 19, 1901.

M

MAARTENS (Maarten) *pseud.* [*i.e.* Joost Marius Willem van der Poorten-Schwartz], *see* SCHWARTZ (Joost Marius Willem van der Poorten-), *pseud.* Maarten Maartens.

MAATSCHAPPIJ DER NEDERLANDSCHE LETTERKUNDE TE LEIDEN, *see* FRANTZEN (J. J. A. A.) [*for* the *Maatschappij der Nederlandsche Letterkunde te Leiden*].

MACALISTER (*Sir* John Young Walker). *1.* February 10, 1923.

MACCARTHY (Desmond). *1.* September 29, 1925.

McCARTHY (Lillah), *afterwards* Mrs. Harley Granville-Barker, *afterwards* Lady Keeble, *see* KEEBLE (Lillah, *Lady*), *formerly* Mrs. Harley Granville-Barker, *née* McCarthy.

MACCOLL (Dugald Sutherland). *1.* February 21, 1909.

MACCOLL (Norman). *1.* December 17, 1883.

M'CORMICK (*Sir* William Symington). *4.* December 1, 1898 —February 14, 1901; 1 undated [incomplete].

—— *from* DAVIDSON (John). *1.* February 12, 1901.

McDONNELL (William Randall), *6th Earl of Antrim. 2.* April 19, 1906; March 28, 1910.

M'FALL (Frances Elizabeth) [Mrs. D. C. M'Fall], *pseud.* Sarah Grand. *1.* June 2, 1894.

MACHEN (Arthur). *1.* February 9, 1922.

MACKAIL (John William). *1.* October 13, 1911.

MACKAY (Donald James), *11th Baron Reay of Reay. 6.* March 28, 1905—September 21, 1919; 1 undated.

MACKENZIE (Compton). *8.* November 18, 1914—February 13, 1924.

—— *to* ROSS (A. G.). *1.* May 25, 1919.

MACKENZIE (Kenneth Augustus Muir), *1st Baron Muir Mackenzie of Delvine. 3.* June 4, 1915—December 2, 1920.

MACLEOD (Lewis Rose) *from* MOORE (George Augustus). *1.* January 7, 1922.
Carbon copy, unsigned.

MACMILLAN & Co., *publishers. 2* telegrams. January 13, 1928; January 14, 1928.

MACMILLAN (Daniel). *1.* January 15, [1928].

MACMILLAN (*Sir* Frederick). *6.* December 7, 1917— January 11, 1918.

MACMILLAN (George A.). *3.* February 25, 1884—August 5, 1910.

MACMILLAN (H. P.). *1.* January 1, 1925.

M'TAGGART (John M'Taggart Ellis). *1.* January 2, 1925.

MADAN (Falconer). *1.* December 20, 1893.

MAGEE (William Kirkpatrick), *pseud.* John Eglinton, *to* GOSSE (Philip). *3.* September 25, 1936—October 2, 1936.

MAGNE (Émile). *2.* August 16, 1920; June 8, 1925.

MAGYAR TUDOMÁNYOS AKADÉMIA [Hungarian Academy of Sciences], *see* SZILY VON NAGYSZIGETH (Coloman) [*for* the Hungarian Academy of Sciences].

MAIGRON (Louis). *1.* October 12, 1916.

MAINE (*Sir* Henry James Sumner). *1.* March 27, 1885.

MAITLAND (Frederic William). *4.* May 16, 1904—November 11, 1906.

MAKOWER (Stanley) *to* HARLAND (Henry). *1.* June 7, 1905.

MALCOLM (*Sir* Ian Zachary) *to* HALDANE (Richard Burdon), *1st Viscount Haldane of Cloan.* *1.* August 8, [1918].

MALLARMÉ (Stéphane). *1.* [1875].

MALLOCK (William Hurrell). *1.* January 19, 1923.

MALMESBURY (James Edward Harris, *5th Earl of*), *see* HARRIS (James Edward), *5th Earl of Malmesbury.*

MANNERS (*Lady* Victoria Alexandra Elizabeth Dorothy). *1.* February 10, [1906].

MANSFIELD (Eleanor Mary Caroline), *Viscountess Sandhurst.* *1.* July 17, 1920.

MANSFIELD (William), *1st Viscount Sandhurst of Sandhurst.* *4.* November 20, 1913—November 5, 1917.

MANTOUX (Paul Joseph). *1.* February 1, 1917.

MANOEL II, *King of Portugal.* *2.* November 25, 1918; June 1, 1924.

MARGARET, *Crown Princess of Sweden.* *1.* May 10, 1918.

MARGUERITTE (Paul). *1.* January 19, 1916.

MARJORIBANKS (Edward), *2nd Baron Tweedmouth of Edington.* *2.* January 28, 1905; December 12, 1905.

MARKHAM (*Sir* Clements Robert). *2.* June 6, 1887; December 2, 1899.

MARSH (*Sir* Edward Howard). *15.* February 4, 1912—July 4, 1922; 1 undated. *Also 1* telegram. September 22, 1919.

——*from* GRAHAM (*Sir* Henry John Lowndes). *1.* February 7, 1902.

MARSHALL (Archibald). *2.* April 12, 1907; September 22, 1919.

MARSHALL (Hugh John Cole). *1.* December 19, 1922.

MARSTON (John Westland). *2.* December 14, 1873; January 3, 1882.

MARSTON (Philip Bourke). *7.* August 2, 1881—December 9, 1885.
> The letter dated August 2, 1881, is signed 'Philip Bourke Marston (per L.C.M.)' [i.e. Louise Chandler Moulton]. The amanuenses employed to write the remaining six letters have not been identified.

MARTIN (Leonard Cyril). *1.* July 11, 1916.

MARY, *Queen Consort of King George V, see* TREFUSIS (*Lady* Mary) [*for* Mary, *Queen Consort of King George V*].

MARZIALS (Théophile Julius Henry). *21.* December 26, 1874—February 22, 1894; 1 undated.

MASEFIELD (John). *18.* November 24, 1911—January 1, 1916; 1 undated.

MASON (Alfred Edward Woodley). *1.* [August 13? 1925].

MAUDE (Lilian Nancy Bache), *née* Price [Mrs. Charles Raymond Maude], *see* PRICE (Lilian Nancy Bache), *afterwards* Mrs. Charles Raymond Maude.

MAURICE (*Sir* Frederick Barton) *to* GOSSE (Philip). *1.* October 2, 1936.

MAUROIS (André) *pseud.* [*i.e.* Émile Salomon Wilhelm Herzog], *see* HERZOG (Émile Salomon Wilhelm), *pseud.* André Maurois.

MAXWELL (*Sir* Herbert Eustace), *7th Bart.* *1.* February 8, 1917.

MAXWELL (Mary Elizabeth), *née* Braddon [Mrs. John Maxwell], *see* BRADDON (Mary Elizabeth), *afterwards* Mrs. John Maxwell.

MAYO (Dermot Robert Wyndham Bourke, *7th Earl of*), *see* BOURKE (Dermot Robert Wyndham), *7th Earl of Mayo.*

MEIKLEJOHN (*Sir* Roderick Sinclair). *12.* May 6, 1908—August 4, 1910.

——*from* LEMON (Arthur) *and* OSBORNE (Charles C.). *1.* April 5, 1909.
> Typewritten copy, unsigned. Enclosed in a letter dated the same day from Charles C. Osborne to Sir Edmund Gosse.

MELCHETT (Alfred Moritz Mond, *1st Baron*), *see* MOND (Alfred Moritz), *1st Baron Melchett of Landford.*

MELVILLE (Lewis) *pseud.* [*i.e.* Lewis Saul Benjamin], *see* BENJAMIN (Lewis Saul), *pseud.* Lewis Melville.

MEREDITH (George) *to* STEPHEN (*Sir* Leslie). *1.* February 14, 1898.
A copy, in Sir Edmund Gosse's hand, attached to a letter dated February 16, 1898, from Sir Leslie Stephen to Sir Edmund Gosse, enclosing the original, which was returned.

MEREDITH (William Maxse). *1.* May 24, 1909.

MERRILL (Charles Edmund). *1.* June 10, 1910.

MERRILL (Stuart Fitzrandolph). *3.* September 1, 1908—June 23, 1912.

MESPOULET (Marguerite). *1.* October 1, 1918.

METTERNICH (Paul Wolff), *Graf Wolff Metternich zur Gracht.* *1.* May 15, 1909.

MEYER (Richard Moritz). *2.* October 23, 1899; June 8, 1909.

MEYNELL (Alice) [Mrs. Wilfrid Meynell]. *10.* December 10, [1896]—March 11, [1905]; 3 undated.

MEYNELL (Wilfrid). *3.* September 28, 1919; January 11, 1925; 1 undated.

MILBANKE (Judith Anne Dorothea), *formerly* Blunt-Lytton, *Baroness Wentworth, see* LYTTON (Judith Anne Dorothea Blunt-), *afterwards* Milbanke, *Baroness Wentworth.*

MILBANKE (Ralph Gordon Noel), *formerly* King-Noel, *2nd Earl of Lovelace, see* KING-NOEL (Ralph Gordon Noel), *afterwards* Milbanke, *2nd Earl of Lovelace.*

MILLE (Pierre). *1.* June 2, 1913.

MILLET (Philippe). *5.* December 21, 1916—September 20, 1925.

MILLS (Arthur Robert), *3rd Baron Hillingdon.* *1.* November 12, 1919.

MILNER (Alfred), *1st Viscount Milner.* *1.* March 27, 1906.

MILNER (Violet Georgina), *Viscountess Milner.* *1.* August 29, 1921.

MILNES (Richard Monckton), *1st Baron Houghton of Great Houghton.* *4.* May 31, 1884—May 20, [1885]; 1 undated.

MILNES (Robert Offley Ashburton Crewe-), *1st Marquis of Crewe.* *57.* September 27, 1894—March 7, 1927. *Also* 2 telegrams. September 21, 1919; August 13, 1925.

—— *to* ASQUITH (Emma Alice Margaret), *Countess of Oxford and Asquith.* *1.* July 21, 1920.

—— *to* BOULTON (*Sir* Harold Edwin), *2nd Bart.* *1.* June 7, 1922.

—— *to* KELLY (James Fitzmaurice-). *1.* December 19, 1918.

—— *to* LANKESTER (*Sir* Edwin Ray). *1.* February 21, 1917.
Enclosed in a letter from Sir Edwin Lankester to Sir Edmund Gosse, dated February 22, [1917].

—— *from* GOSSE (*Sir* Edmund William). *1.* Undated.

—— *from* HARRISON (Frederic). *1.* September 21, 1919.
Typewritten transcript.

MINTO (William). *5.* March 10, 1874—March 2, 1885.

MITCHELL (*Sir* Peter Chalmers). *1.* September 19, 1919.

MITFORD (Algernon Bertram Freeman-), *1st Baron Redesdale of Redesdale.* *95.* March 30, 1908—August 10, 1916.

—— *to* HALDANE (Richard Burdon), *1st Viscount Haldane of Cloan.* *1.* August 10, 1916.

MITFORD (Clementine Gertrude Helen Freeman-), *Baroness Redesdale.* *1* telegram. August 17, 1916.

MITFORD (Daphne Freeman-), *afterwards* Baroness Denham. *1.* August 17, 1916.

MITFORD (Thomas David Freeman-). *2.* June 24, 1916; January 7, 1917.

MOCKEL (Albert). *3.* March 28, 1908—January 9, 1925.

—— *to* BRUNOT (Ferdinand). *1* telegram. November 28, 1925.

MOLBECH (Christian Knud Frederik). *4.* February 5, 1876—September 5, 1879.

MOLESWORTH (William Nassau). *1.* March 20, 1885.

MONCRIEFF (Charles Kenneth Michael Scott). *3.* December 11, 1917—August 12, 1925.

MOND (Alfred Moritz), *1st Baron Melchett of Landford.* *3.* [November? 1908]—January 1, 1925.

MONK BRETTON (John William Dodson, *2nd Baron*), *see* DODSON (John William), *2nd Baron Monk Bretton of Conyboro and Hurstpierpoint.*

MONKHOUSE (William Cosmo). *1.* December 1, 1879.

—— *to* LANE (John). *1.* August 21, 1890.

MONTAGU (John Walter Edward Douglas-Scott-), *2nd Baron Montagu of Beaulieu.* *4.* [December 27, 1908]; January 31, 1912; 2 undated.

MONTEAGLE OF BRANDON (Thomas Spring Rice, *2nd Baron*), *see* RICE (Thomas Spring), *2nd Baron Monteagle of Brandon.*

MONTGOMERIE (Archibald Seton), *16th Earl of Eglinton and Winton.* *1.* April 27, 1920.

MOORE (George Augustus). *126.* [July 8, 1887]—February 29, 1928; 28 undated.
The letter of February 29, 1928, is signed 'George Moore p.p. M.K.' [*i.e.* Mona Kingdon].

—— *to* GOSSE (Ellen, *Lady*). *2.* (July 4, 1896); December 25, [1913].

—— *to* GOSSE (Philip). *11.* January 6, 1922—November 17, (1932).
The letters of January 6, 1922, and November 1, 1932, are signed 'George Moore p.p. M.K.' [*i.e.* Mona Kingdon].

—— *to* MACLEOD (Lewis Rose). *1.* January 7, 1922.
Carbon copy, unsigned.

—— *see also* PALMER (E.) [*for* George Augustus Moore].

MOORE (*Sir* Norman), *1st Bart. 1.* May 26, 1899.

MOORE (Thomas Sturge). *1.* February, 1907.

MORGAN (Charles Langbridge) *to* GOSSE (Philip). *1.* January 24, 1933.

MORISON (James Augustus Cotter). *46.* October 18, 1883—[January 13, 1888].

MORITZ (Neville). *1.* [March] 28, 1878.

MORLEY (John), *1st Viscount Morley of Blackburn. 24.* March 6, 1873—December 5, 1918.

—— *to* COLVIN (*Sir* Sidney). *1.* February 8, 1883.

—— *to* HALDANE (Richard Burdon), *1st Viscount Haldane of Cloan. 1.* December 27, 1916.

—— *to* [KELLY (James Fitzmaurice-)?]. *1.* September 19, 1919.

—— *to* Ross (A. G.). *1.* December 18, 1918.

MORRIS (*Sir* Lewis). *2.* October 29, 1887; November 30, 1890.

MORRISON (William Douglas). *1.* May 29, 1918.

MOULTON (Ellen Louise Chandler) [Mrs. William U. Moulton]. *2.* July 30, [1881]; [August, 1881].

MOUNT EDGCUMBE (William Henry Edgcumbe, *4th Earl of*), *see* EDGCUMBE (William Henry), *4th Earl of Mount Edgcumbe.*

MÜLLER (Friedrich Max). *1.* October 1, 1890.

—— *to* GOSSE (Philip Henry). *1.* October 18, [1869].

MUENIER (Pierre Alexis). *1.* August 19, 1926.

MUIR MACKENZIE (Kenneth Augustus Muir Mackenzie, *1st Baron*), *see* MACKENZIE (Kenneth Augustus Muir), *1st Baron Muir Mackenzie of Delvine.*

MUNBY (Arthur Joseph). *2*. December 13, 1882; July 7, 1884.

MUNCH (Andreas). *3*. March 12, 1874—January 21, 1875.

MUNRO (David A.) *to* SMITH (Roswell). *1*. May 24, 1889.
Typewritten copy. Enclosed in a letter [June? 1889] from Viscount Wolseley to Sir Edmund Gosse.

MUNRO (Hugh Andrew Johnstone). *1*. February 18, 1884.

MUNTHE (Axel). *1*. June 11, [1916?].

MURRAY (Andrew Graham), *1st Viscount Dunedin*. *11*. [December 1, 1913]—August 10, [1925]; 2 undated.

MURRAY (David Christie). *1*. February 26, 1897.

MURRAY (George Gilbert Aimé). *7*. May 29, 1895—October 2, 1919.

MURRAY (*Sir* George Herbert). *6*. January 9, 1917—March 31, 1927.

—— *to* SANDERSON (Thomas Henry), *1st Baron Sanderson of Armthorpe*. *4*. July 20, 1921—October 16, 1922.
Letter dated July 20, 1921: enclosed in Lord Sanderson's letter to Sir Edmund Gosse dated the following day.

—— *from* PROTHERO (Rowland Edmund), *1st Baron Ernle of Chelsea*. *1*. May 5, 1922.

MURRAY (*Sir* James Augustus Henry). *1*. September 30, 1902.

MURRAY (John). *2*. November 9, 1886; 1 undated.

MURRAY (John George Stewart-), *8th Duke of Atholl*. *3*. July 13, 1922—November 2, 1922.

MURRY (John Middleton). *3*. May 12, 1922—December 22, 1927.

MYERS (Frederic William Henry). *9*. July 24, 1881—November 4, 1883.

N

NAIDU (Sarojini) [Mme. M. G. Naidu]. *1*. September 21, 1920.

NEIL (Robert Alexander). *2*. May 27, 1884; March 24, 1891.

NETTLESHIP (John Trivett). *1*. May 8, 1890.

NEVILL (*Lady* Dorothy Fanny). *35*. [September] 2, [1892]—[March] 6, [1913]; 8 undated.

NEVILL (Horace John). *1*. December 18, 1913.

NEVILL (Meresia Dorothy Augusta). *1*. [December 15, 1913].

NEVILL (Ralph Henry). *3.* December 15, 1913—October 31, 1922.

NEWBOLT (*Sir* Henry John). *15.* January 24, 1903—May 17, 1922; 2 undated.

NEWCOMBE (Bertha) *to* GOSSE (Ellen, *Lady*). *1.* March 8, (1900).

NEWTON (Alfred). *1.* January 1, 1891.

NEWTON (Evelyn Caroline Legh, *Baroness*), *see* LEGH (Evelyn Caroline), *Baroness Newton.*

NEWTON (Thomas Wodehouse Legh, *2nd Baron*), *see* LEGH (Thomas Wodehouse), *2nd Baron Newton of Newton-in-Makerfield.*

NICHOLS (Robert Malise Bowyer). *21.* October 23—24, 1917—June 24, 1922. *Also 1* telegram. September 20, 1919.

NICHOLSON (Brinsley). *8.* August, 1891—April 14, 1892.

NICOLL (*Sir* William Robertson). *1.* September 21, [1905?].

NICOLSON (Harold). *2.* March 10, 1924; January 1, 1928.

NIELSEN (Harald). *1.* April 23, 1918.

NOCQ (Henry). *1.* September 17, 1916.

NOGUCHI (Yone). *2.* March 14, (1913); June 1, 1915.

NOLHAC (Anet Marie Pierre Girauld de). *2.* January 11, 1924; October 24, 1924.

NORMAN (Arthur). *2.* June 27, 1921; July 28, 1926.

NORRIS (E. F.). *2.* February 21, 1927; February 23, 1927.

NORRIS (William Edward). *65.* May 31, 1891—August 15, 1925.

NORTHAMPTON (William George Spencer Scott Compton, *5th Marquis of*) *see* COMPTON (William George Spencer Scott), *5th Marquis of Northampton.*

NORTHBROOK (Thomas George Baring, *1st Earl of*), *see* BARING (Thomas George), *1st Earl of Northbrook.*

NORTHCLIFFE (Alfred Charles William Harmsworth, *1st Viscount*), *see* HARMSWORTH (Alfred Charles William), *1st Viscount Northcliffe of St. Peter.*

NORTHUMBERLAND (Henry George Percy, *7th Duke of*), *see* PERCY (Henry George), *7th Duke of Northumberland.*

NORWAY, *Royal Norwegian Legation, London. 1.* February 14, 1928.

NOYES (Alfred). *26.* April 3, 1907—September 21, 1927.

NOYES (Garnett) [Mrs. Alfred Noyes]. *4.* December 11, [1912]—December 24, [1912].

O

O'Brien (Richard Barry). *1.* March 6, 1918.

O'Connor (Daniel). *1.* May 10, 1915.

Ogilvy (Henrietta Blanche), *Countess of Airlie. 18.* October 23, [1913]—November 20, 1920; 1 undated.

O'Grady (Frederick Standish). *1.* April 13, 1896.

Oliphant (Margaret Oliphant Wilson) [Mrs. Francis Wilson Oliphant]. *1.* July 10, [1883].

Oliver (Frederick Scott). *2.* May 4, 1921; May 5, 1921.

Onley (Onley Savill). *1.* January 17, 1884.

Onslow (Richard William Alan), *5th Earl of Onslow. 2.* April 8, 1926; April 13, 1926.

Onslow (William Hillier), *4th Earl of Onslow. 5.* Undated.

—— *to* Bourke (Dermot Robert Wyndham), *7th Earl of Mayo. 1.* July 6, 1907.

Order of St. John of Jerusalem in England, *see* Hudson (*Sir* Robert Arundell) [*for* the Joint War Committee of the British Red Cross Society and the Order of St. John of Jerusalem in England].

Ording (Fredrik). *1.* January 30, 1918.

Orford (Robert Horace Walpole, *5th Earl of*), *see* Walpole (Robert Horace), *5th Earl of Orford.*

Orpen (Thomas H.). *1.* February 22, 1884.

Osborne (Charles C.). *3.* March 31, 1909—April 6, 1909.
Letter of April 5, 1909: enclosed is a typewritten copy, dated the same day, of a letter from Arthur Lemon and Charles C. Osborne to Sir Roderick Sinclair Meiklejohn, unsigned.

—— *see also* Lemon (Arthur) *and* Osborne (Charles C.).

Osbourne (Isobel Stuart), *afterwards* Mrs. Joseph Dwight Strong, *see* Strong (Isobel Stuart), *née* Osbourne [Mrs. Joseph Dwight Strong].

O'Shaughnessy (Arthur William Edgar). *14.* August 31, 1872—March 5, 1880; 2 undated.

Ossiannilsson (Karl Gustav). *7.* March 23, 1902—January 8, 1919.

Ottley (Robert Lawrence). *1.* February 3, [1895?].

Oxford, *University, Taylor Institution, see* Wright (Joseph) [*for* the Curators of the Taylor Institution].

Oxford and Asquith (Emma Alice Margaret Asquith, *Countess of*), *see* Asquith (Emma Alice Margaret), *Countess of Oxford and Asquith.*

Oxford and Asquith (Herbert Henry Asquith, *1st Earl of*), *see* Asquith (Herbert Henry), *1st Earl of Oxford and Asquith.*

P

P.E.N. CLUB, *see* SCOTT (M.) [*for* the P.E.N. Club].

PAGE (Emily). *1.* November 27, 1908.

PAGE (Thomas Ethelbert). *1.* December 25, 1927.

PAGET (Francis), *Bishop of Oxford.* *1.* May 25, 1892.

PAGET (Violet), *pseud.* Vernon Lee. *2.* February 12, 1906; 1 undated [incomplete].

PALACIO VALDÉS (Armando). *8.* August 8, 1890—November 22, 1916.

—— *to* HEINEMANN (William). *1.* July 14, 1894.

PALGRAVE (Francis Turner). *5.* July 11, 1877—January 14, 1889; 1 undated.

—— *to* "Dear Maria." *1.* July 1, 1871.
The addressee has not been identified.

PALMER (E.) [*for* George Augustus Moore] *to* GOSSE (Philip). *1.* March 17, 1932.

PALMSTIERNA (*Friherre* Erik Kule). *1.* April 28, 1923.

PANGE (*Comte* Jean de). *4.* September 16, 1919—November 22, 1925.

—— *to* BELLOWS (William). *1.* November 4, 1921.

PANGE (Pauline de), *Comtesse Jean de Pange, née* de Broglie. *3.* [October?] 1921—November 16, 1925.

—— *to* BELLOWS (William). *3.* August 26, 1921—November 11, 1925.

—— *to* GOSSE (Ellen, *Lady*). *1.* [December] 15, 1921.
Dated incorrectly '15 Xe 1921.'

PARIS, *University, see* LAPIE (P.) [*for* the University of Paris].

PARKER (*Sir* Gilbert), *1st Bart.* *4.* December 17, 1897—May 1, 1924.

—— *to* ROSS (A. G.). *1.* May 8, 1919.

PARKER (Walter A.). *1.* November 29, 1870.

PARMOOR (Charles Alfred Cripps, *1st Baron*), *see* CRIPPS (Charles Alfred), *1st Baron Parmoor of Frieth.*

PARRY (*Sir* Frederick Sydney). *30.* January 5, 1901—October 29, 1902; 2 undated.
Enclosed in a letter dated June 10, 1902, is a typewritten copy, dated the same day, of a letter from Sir F. S. Parry to A. Llewelyn Roberts.

—— *to* ROBERTS (A. Llewelyn). *1.* June 10, 1902.
Typewritten copy. Enclosed in a letter from Sir F. S. Parry to Sir Edmund Gosse, dated the same day.

PATER (Clara). *1.* June 24, 1896.

PATER (Hester M.). *2.* September 22, [1919]; 1 undated.

PATER (Walter Horatio). *11.* May 25, [1877]—[June 20, 1893]; 4 undated.

PATERSON (William Romaine), *pseud.* Benjamin Swift. *1.* May 15, 1917.

PATMORE (Coventry Kersey Dighton). *50.* January 11, 1881—November 9, 1896.

PATMORE (Harriet) [Mrs. Coventry Kersey Dighton Patmore]. *1.* November 27, 1896.

PATTISON (Andrew Seth Pringle-), *formerly* Seth, *see* SETH (Andrew), *afterwards* Andrew Seth Pringle-Pattison.

PAUL (C. Kegan) & Co., *publishers.* *1.* October 8, 1878.

PAUL (Charles Kegan). *4.* March 5, 1881—February 21, 1884.

PAWLING (Sydney S.). *3.* July 11, 1902—March 27, 1922.

PAYNE (de Vincheles Payen-). *3.* June 2, 1919 [2]; January 7, 1922.

PEEL (*Lady* Adelaide Margaret Delia), *née* Spencer, *see* SPENCER (*Lady* Adelaide Margaret Delia), *afterwards* Peel.

PEEL (Arthur George Villiers). *1.* March 21, 1926.

PEEL (Arthur Wellesley), *1st Viscount Peel of Sandy.* *2.* June 5, 1905; August 5, 1905.

PELHAM (Jocelyn Brudenell), *6th Earl of Chichester.* *1.* Undated.

PELHAM (Thomas Henry William) *from* DOBSON (Henry Austin). *1.* January 17, 1898.

PEMBER (Edward Henry). *13.* February 4, 1910—August 14, 1910.

PEMBROKE (George Robert Charles Herbert, *13th Earl of*), *see* HERBERT (George Robert Charles), *13th Earl of Pembroke.*

PENN CLUB, *see* FURNESS (Horace Howard) [*for* the Penn Club].

PENNELL (Elizabeth) [Mrs. Joseph Pennell]. *1.* June 18, 1917.

PENNELL (Joseph). *1.* August 16, 1924.

PENTLAND (John Sinclair, *1st Baron*), *see* SINCLAIR (John), *1st Baron Pentland of Lyth.*

PERCY (*Lord* Eustace Sutherland Campbell). *2.* April 21, 1925; April 26, [1925].

PERCY (Henry George), *7th Duke of Northumberland.* *3.* August 10, 1907—January 13, 1910.

PERRY (Thomas Sergeant). *1.* November 10, 1886.

PETTER (John). *1.* March 2, 1884.

PEZZO (Anne Charlotte Gustava del), *Duchèssa di Cajanello, formerly* fru G. E. Edgren, *née* Leffler, *see* LEFFLER (Anne Charlotte Gustava), *afterwards* fru G. E. Edgren, *afterwards* Duchèssa di Cajanello.

PHILLIPS (*Sir* Claude). *2.* March 21, 1916; September 22, 1919.

PHILLIPS (Stephen). *6.* [December 5, 1899]—[July 25, 1901].

PHILPOTT (Henry), *Bishop of Worcester. 1.* December 3, 1883.

PILKINGTON (J. Holme). *1.* February 8, 1884.

PINERO (*Sir* Arthur Wing). *27.* May 2, 1893—December 6, 1917.

PINKER (James B.). *1.* August 2, 1916.

PLUNKET (David Robert), *1st Baron Rathmore of Shanganagh. 1.* June 26, 1914.

PLUNKETT (*Sir* Horace Curzon). *2.* May 27, 1908; January 11, 1925.

PLYMOUTH (Robert George Windsor-Clive, *1st Earl of*), *see* CLIVE (Robert George Windsor-), *1st Earl of Plymouth.*

POEL (William). *1.* June 23, 1923.

POLIGNAC (Winnaretta de), *Princess. 3.* July 20, 1911—December 30, 1919. *Also 1* telegram. July 27, 1911.

POLLARD (Alfred William) *to* WISE (Thomas James). *2.* [September 16? 1909]; January 7, 1913.

   Letter dated [September 16? 1909]: written on the back is a letter from T. J. Wise to Sir Edmund Gosse, dated September 17, 1909.

POLLOCK (Ernest Murray), *1st Viscount Hanworth of Hanworth. 4.* August 5, 1924—September 11, 1927.

POLLOCK (*Sir* Frederick), *3rd Bart. 7.* January 15, 1898—August 11, 1925.

POLLOCK (Walter Herries). *1.* December 7, 1904.

—— *see also* LANG (Andrew) *to* POLLOCK [Walter Herries Pollock?].

PONSONBY (Frederick Edward Grey), *1st Baron Sysonby of Wonersh. 3.* December 12, 1916—April 13, 1918.

—— *to* HALDANE (Richard Burdon), *1st Viscount Haldane of Cloan. 1.* November 30, 1916.

PONSONBY (Mary Elizabeth, *Lady*). *2.* December 20, 1904; July 6, 1906.

PORTAL (*Sir* William Wyndham), *2nd Bart.* *1.* February 3, 1926.

PORTER (James). *1.* May 22, 1885.

PORTSMOUTH (Newton Wallop, *6th Earl of*), *see* WALLOP (Newton), *6th Earl of Portsmouth.*

POTTER (George R.) *to* GOSSE (Philip). *1.* March 30, 1930.

POWELL (Frederick York). *1.* January 12, 1900.

POWELL (George Herbert) *to* LISTER (Thomas), *4th Baron Ribblesdale of Gisburne Park.* *1.* May 20, 1909.

Enclosed in a letter from Lord Ribblesdale to Sir Edmund Gosse, dated May 26, [1909].

POWELL (Nancy F.). *1.* March 11, 1923.

POWIS (Edward James Herbert, *3rd Earl of*), *see* HERBERT (Edward James), *3rd Earl of Powis.*

PRÉVOST (Marcel). *4.* July 13, 1898—August 20, 1899; 1 undated.

PRICE (Lilian Nancy Bache), *afterwards* Mrs. Charles Raymond Maude *to* GOSSE (Philip). *1.* March 30, 1938.

PRIMROSE (Archibald Philip), *5th Earl of Rosebery.* *4.* March 3, 1907—November 2, 1917.

PRINCE (Helen Choati). *1.* July 11, 1913.

PRINGLE-PATTISON (Andrew Seth), *formerly* Seth, *see* SETH (Andrew), *afterwards* Andrew Seth Pringle-Pattison.

PROTHERO (*Sir* George Walter). *10.* December 13, 1899—January 2, 1913; 2 undated.

PROTHERO (Rowland Edmund), *1st Baron Ernle of Chelsea.* *7.* June 11, 1898—January 1, 1925.

—— *to* BENSON (Dorothea Mary Roby), *Baroness Charnwood.* *1.* December 22, 1925.

Signed 'Ernle p.p. A.L.M.'

—— *to* MURRAY (*Sir* George Herbert). *1.* May 5, 1922.

PROUST (Marcel). *1.* [March 12, 1921].

Q

QUICKSWOOD (Hugh Richard Heathcote Gascoyne-Cecil, *1st Baron*), *see* CECIL (Hugh Richard Heathcote Gascoyne-), *1st Baron Quickswood of Clothall.*

QUILLER-COUCH (*Sir* Arthur Thomas). *5.* June 14, 1892—August 17, 1925.

R

Rackham (Arthur). *2.* June 1, 1918; October 19, 1918.

Radnor (Helen Matilda Pleydell-Bouverie, *Countess of*), *see* Bouverie (Helen Matilda Pleydell-), *Countess of Radnor.*

Raffalovich (Mark André). *1.* [1884?].

Rajon (Paul Adolphe). *5.* February 7, 1881—November 16, 1881.

Raleigh (*Sir* Walter Alexander). *15.* November 30, 1889—February 10, 1921.

—— *to* Gosse (Ellen, *Lady*). *1.* September 16, (1889).

Ramsay (*Sir* Malcolm Graham). *46.* March 9, 1902—March 10, 1908.

Raper (J. E.). *1.* February 28, 1916.

Rathmore (David Robert Plunket, *1st Baron*), *see* Plunket (David Robert), *1st Baron Rathmore of Shanganagh.*

Rayleigh (Robert John Strutt, *4th Baron*), *see* Strutt (Robert John), *4th Baron Rayleigh of Terling Place.*

Reay (Donald James Mackay, *11th Baron*), *see* Mackay (Donald James), *11th Baron Reay of Reay.*

Recke (Ernst Frederik Vilhelm von der). *2.* September 10, 1873; March 21, 1890.

Redesdale (Algernon Bertram Freeman-Mitford, *1st Baron*), *see* Mitford (Algernon Bertram Freeman-), *1st Baron Redesdale of Redesdale.*

Redesdale (Clementine Gertrude Helen Freeman-Mitford, *Baroness*), *see* Mitford (Clementine Gertrude Helen Freeman-), *Baroness Redesdale.*

Rees (Leonard). *2.* January 29, 1923; 1 undated.

Régnier (Henri François Joseph de). *5.* January (13), 1903—October (27), 1918.

Reid (Robert Threshie), *1st Earl Loreburn. 3.* March 13, 1913—September 14, 1913.

Reid (Thomas Mayne). *1.* [September 21, 1883].

Rennell (James Rennell Rodd, *1st Baron*), *see* Rodd (James Rennell), *1st Baron Rennell of Rodd.*

Repplier (Agnes). *5.* October 24, 1888—February 1, 1925.

Revelstoke (John Baring, *2nd Baron*), *see* Baring (John), *2nd Baron Revelstoke of Revelstoke.*

Revue des Deux Mondes. *1.* October 19, 1916.

Rew (*Sir* Robert Henry). *1.* November 7, 1920.

Reynolds (Myra). *2.* February 20, 1902; July 4, 1902.

RHYS (Ernest). *1*. July 9, [1894].

RIBBLESDALE (Thomas Lister, *4th Baron*), *see* LISTER (Thomas), *4th Baron Ribblesdale of Gisburne Park*.

RICE (Thomas Spring), *2nd Baron Monteagle of Brandon*. *1*. January 3, 1905.

RICHARDS (Franklin Thomas Grant). *1*. March 20, 1902.

RICHMOND (*Sir* Bruce Lyttelton). *2*. [January, 1920]; January 2, [1928].

RICHMOND (*Sir* William Blake). *3*. January 23, 1897— November 24, 1915.

RICKETTS (Charles). *1*. Undated.

RIDGE (William Pett). *1*. Undated.

RIDLEY (Matthew White), *2nd Viscount Ridley*. *1*. Undated.

RIGGS (Kate Douglas) [Mrs. George Christopher Riggs], *formerly* Mrs. Samuel Bradley Wiggin, *see* WIGGIN (Kate Douglas) [Mrs. Samuel Bradley Wiggin], *afterwards* Mrs. George Christopher Riggs.

RITCHIE (Anne Isabella, *Lady*), *née* Thackeray, *see* THACKERAY (Anne Isabella), *afterwards* Lady Ritchie.

RITCHIE (Hester). *1*. September 9, [1923?].

RIVIERE (Briton). *1*. February 7, 1884.

ROBB (Elvy) & WELCH, *solicitors*. *1*. July 26, 1926.

ROBERTS (A. Llewelyn) *to* LANG (Andrew). *1*. January 4, 1890.

—— *from* PARRY (*Sir* Frederick Sydney). *1*. June 10, 1902. Typewritten copy. Enclosed in a letter from Sir F. S. Parry to Sir Edmund Gosse, dated the same day.

—— [*for* the Royal Literary Fund]. *3*. June 12, 1902— May 17, 1915.

ROBERTS (Frederick Sleigh), *1st Earl Roberts of Kandahar, Pretoria and Waterford*. *1*. May 29, 1913.

ROBERTSON (*Sir* George Scott). *1*. February 14, 1899.

ROBERTSON (John George). *1*. September 28, 1925.

ROBINSON (Agnes Mary Frances), *afterwards* Mme. James Darmesteter, *afterwards* Mme. Pierre Émile Duclaux. *45*. January 10, 1879—October 11, [1922]; 12 undated.

—— *to* GOSSE (*Sir* Edmund William) *and* GOSSE (Ellen, *Lady*). *1*. Undated.

—— *to* GOSSE (Ellen, *Lady*). *1*. January 8, 1879.

ROBINSON (Edwin Arlington). *1*. November 1, 1923.

ROBINSON (Frances Mabel). *7*. [1890]—January 22, [1904].

ROD (Edouard). *7*. October 26, 1903—February 23, 1904.

RODD (James Rennell), *1st Baron Rennell of Rodd*. *1*. February 21, 1921.

RØRDAM (Valdemar). *1*. April 25, 1918.

ROLLESTON (*Sir* Humphry Davy), *1st Bart*. *2*. December 11, 1924; August 9, 1925.

ROMANES (George John). *2*. March 25, (1886); October 23, 1886.

RONALD (W. T.). *1*. June 23, 1890.

ROOT (Elihu). *1*. August 29, 1914.

ROSEBERY (Archibald Philip Primrose, *5th Earl of*), *see* PRIMROSE (Archibald Philip), *5th Earl of Rosebery*.

ROSNY (J. H.) *aîné, pseud.* [*i.e.* Joseph Henri Honoré Boëx-Borel], *see* BOËX-BOREL (Joseph Henri Honoré), *pseud.* J. H. Rosny *aîné*.

ROSS (A. G.). *1*. May 15, 1908.

—— *from* BENSON (Arthur Christopher). *1*. May 14, 1919.

—— *from* BOOKER (Robert A. D.) [*for* Cosmo Gordon Lang, *Archbishop of York*]. *1*. December 18, 1918.

—— *from* CANE (Arthur Beresford). *1*. May 27, 1919.

—— *from* COLVIN (*Sir* Sidney). *1*. [*c.* November 30, 1918].

—— *from* CONRAD (Joseph). *1*. May 9, 1919.

—— *from* DICKSEE (*Sir* Francis Bernard). *1*. January 25, 1919.

—— *from* FISHER (Adrienne). *1*. May 8, 1919.

—— *from* FRAMPTON (*Sir* George James). *1*. May 10, 1919.

—— *from* FRAZER (*Sir* James George). *1*. September 27, 1919.

—— *from* GUINEY (Louise Imogen). *1*. May 18, 1919.

—— *from* HAGGARD (*Sir* Henry Rider). *1*. December 19, 1918.

—— *from* HEWLETT (Maurice Henry). *1*. December 18, 1918.

—— *from* HUNT (William). *1*. December 18, 1918.

—— *from* JOHNSTON (*Sir* Harry Hamilton). *1*. May 14, 1919.

—— *from* KELLY (James Fitzmaurice-). *1*. December 20, 1918.

—— *from* MACKENZIE (Compton). *1*. May 25, 1919.

—— *from* MORLEY (John), *1st Viscount Morley of Blackburn*. *1*. December 18, 1918.

—— *from* PARKER (*Sir* Gilbert), *1st Bart*. *1*. May 8, 1919.

—— *from* SMITH (John Alexander). *1*. January 10, 1919.

—— *from* SMITH (Logan Pearsall). *1*. May 13, 1919.

—— *from* SPENCER (Charles Robert), *6th Earl Spencer*. *1.* December 18, 1918.

—— *from* STEPHEN (*Sir* Herbert), *2nd Bart*. *1.* December 18, 1918.

—— *from* THORPE (Nelly) [Mrs. Roby Thorpe]. *1.* January 13, 1919.

—— *from* VANE-TEMPEST-STEWART (Charles Stewart Henry), *7th Marquis of Londonderry*. *1.* December 17, 1918.

—— *from* VANE-TEMPEST-STEWART (Theresa Susey Helen), *Marchioness of Londonderry*. *1.* December 28, 1918.

—— *from* WARREN (*Sir* Thomas Herbert). *1.* December 18, 1918.

—— *from* WAUGH (Arthur). *1.* May 11, 1919.

—— *from* WELLS (Herbert George). *1.* [May? 1919].

Ross (*Sir* Frederick William Leith-). *7.* February 14, 1912— March 13, 1913.

Ross (Robert Baldwin). *10.* April 19, 1907—September 14, 1918.

ROTHENSTEIN (*Sir* William). *9.* March 23, 1898—August 12, 1925.

ROYAL LITERARY FUND, *see* ROBERTS (A. Llewelyn) [*for* the Royal Literary Fund].

ROYAL SOCIETY OF LITERATURE OF THE UNITED KINGDOM, *see* AMES (Percy Willoughby) [*for* the Royal Society of Literature of the United Kingdom].

—— *see* WAGSTAFF (W. H.) [*for* the Royal Society of Literature of the United Kingdom].

ROYÈRE (Jean). *3.* March 6, 1928—March 22, 1928.

Roz (Firmin). *1.* July 8, [1906].

RUDLER (Gustave). *1.* February 1, 1925.

RUSSELL (Adeline Marie), *Duchess of Bedford*. *1.* March 26, 1912.

RUSSELL (George William Erskine). *3.* June 11, 1917; 2 undated.

RUSSELL (James Samuel Risien). *1.* November 4, 1908.

RUST (John Cyprian). *1.* April 7, 1885.

S

SABATIER (Paul). *3.* October 14, 1916—November 6, 1921.
Letter of October 14, 1916: enclosed in a letter from Paul Sabatier to William Bellows, dated January 9, 1922.

—— *to* BELLOWS (William). *4.* July 29, 1921—January 9, 1922.

Letter of January 9, 1922: enclosed is a letter from Paul Sabatier to Sir Edmund Gosse, dated October 14, 1916.

—— *to* GOSSE (Ellen, *Lady*). *1.* November 22, 1921.

SACKVILLE (Josephine Victoria Sackville-West, *Baroness*), *see* WEST (Josephine Victoria Sackville-), *Baroness Sackville.*

SACKVILLE (Lionel Edward Sackville-West, *3rd Baron*), *see* WEST (Lionel Edward Sackville-), *3rd Baron Sackville of Knole.*

SÆLAND (S.) *from* LINDLEY (*Sir* Francis Oswald). *1.* March 30, 1928.

Typewritten copy. Enclosed in a letter bearing the same date from Sir Francis Lindley to Sir Edmund Gosse.

ST. ALBANS (Grace Beauclerk, *Duchess of*), *see* BEAUCLERK (Grace), *Duchess of St. Albans.*

SAINTSBURY (George Edward Bateman). *33.* October 13, [1882]—September 6, 1925; 6 undated.

SALTER (Clare A.). *1.* September 20, 1905.

SAMBOURNE (Edward Linley). *1.* February 27, 1904.

SAMPSON (George). *2.* October 17, 1927; October 19, 1927.

SANDARS (Samuel). *1.* October 25, 1884.

SANDERSON (C. L. G.). *1.* March 23, 1923.

SANDERSON (Thomas Henry), *1st Baron Sanderson of Armthorpe.* *68.* December 9, 1911—March 16, 1923.

Letter of June 30, 1919: enclosed is a letter from Douglas, 1st Earl Haig, to Lord Sanderson, dated June 27, 1919.

Letter of July 21, 1921: enclosed is a letter from Sir George H. Murray to Lord Sanderson, dated July 20, 1921.

—— *from* HAIG (Douglas), *1st Earl Haig.* *1.* June 27, 1919.

Enclosed in a letter from Lord Sanderson to Sir Edmund Gosse, dated June 30, 1919.

—— *from* MURRAY (*Sir* George Herbert). *4.* July 20, 1921—October 16, 1922.

Letter dated July 20, 1921: enclosed in Lord Sanderson's letter to Sir Edmund Gosse dated the following day.

—— *see also* GRENFELL (Francis Wallace), *1st Baron Grenfell of Kilvey to* SANDERSON [Thomas Henry Sanderson, *1st Baron Sanderson of Armthorpe?*].

SANDHURST (Eleanor Mary Caroline Mansfield, *Viscountess*), *see* MANSFIELD (Eleanor Mary Caroline), *Viscountess Sandhurst.*

SANDHURST (William Mansfield, *1st Viscount*), *see* MANSFIELD (William), *1st Viscount Sandhurst of Sandhurst.*

SARGENT (John Singer). *7.* January 28, (1886)—[December 4, 1916].

SASSOON (Siegfried Lorraine). *22.* September 14, [1916]— December 23, [1927]; 6 undated.

—— *from* THORNYCROFT (Agatha, *Lady*). *1.* June 8, [1927?].

SATOW (*Sir* Ernest Mason). *1.* November 1, 1917.

SAUMAREZ (James St. Vincent), *4th Baron de Saumarez of Saumarez. 1.* Undated.

SAURAT (Denis). *1.* November 18, 1925.

SAVA (A. B.). *3.* August 16, 1926; August 17, 1926; 1 undated.

SAVAGE (Richard Cloudesley). *1.* March 3, 1926.

SAYER (Alfred L.). *1.* April 4, 1905.

SCHARF (*Sir* George). *2.* May 5, 1885; May 22, 1885.

SCHLESINGER (Sylvia). *1.* September 21, [1919].

SCHLUMBERGER (Jean). *2.* November 9, (1915); February 12, [1916?].

SCHWAB (Raymond). *2.* March 16, 1914; March 31, 1914.

SCHWARTZ (Ada van der Poorten-), *see* SCHWARTZ (Joost Marius Willem van der Poorten-), *pseud.* Maarten Maartens, *and* SCHWARTZ (Ada van der Poorten-).

SCHWARTZ (Joost Marius Willem van der Poorten-), *pseud.* Maarten Maartens. *30.* April 17, 1892—August 15, 1914.
Five of the letters are typewritten copies.

—— *to* GOSSE (*Sir* Edmund William) *and* GOSSE (Ellen, *Lady*). *2.* June 26, 1911; May 19, 1913.
The letter of June 26, 1911, is a typewritten copy.

—— *from* GOSSE (*Sir* Edmund William). *1.* December 27, 1898.
Typewritten copy.

—— *and* SCHWARTZ (Ada van der Poorten-) *to* GOSSE (*Sir* Edmund William) *and* GOSSE (Ellen, *Lady*). *1.* December 19, 1907.
Typewritten copy.

—— *see also* GOSSE (*Sir* Edmund William) *and* SCHWARTZ (Joost Marius Willem van der Poorten-), *pseud.* Maarten Maartens.

SCHWOB (Mayer André Marcel). *5.* July 31, 1903— January 2, 1905.

SCOTLAND (D.) [*for* Hugh Lupus Grosvenor, *1st Duke of Westminster*]. *1.* March 20, 1884.

SCOTT (M.) [*for* the P.E.N. Club]. *1.* Undated.

SCOTT (William Bell). *15.* February 27, [1871]—September 15, 1882.

SEAMAN (*Sir* Owen), *1st Bart.* *9.* February 24, 1900—August 13, 1925.

—— *to* BENJAMIN (Lewis Saul), *pseud.* Lewis Melville. *1.* November 24, 1915.

—— *to* WATSON (Henry Brereton Marriott). *1.* October 8, 1914.

SEARLE (Charles Edward). *17.* November 2, 1883—March 15, 1884; 12 undated.

SÉCHÉ (Léon). *1.* (December 6, 1903).

SELBY (William Court Gully, *1st Viscount*), *see* GULLY (William Court), *1st Viscount Selby.*

SELIGMAN (Sybil Vincent). *2* telegrams. September 20, 1919; January 5, 1925.

SETH (Andrew), *afterwards* Andrew Seth Pringle-Pattison. *1.* May 22, 1921.

SETON (Walter W.) [*for* University College, London]. *1.* February 12, 1917.

SHAFTESBURY (Constance Sibell Ashley-Cooper, *Countess of*), *see* COOPER (Constance Sibell Ashley-), *Countess of Shaftesbury.*

SHANKS (Edward Richard Buxton). *6.* July 29, 1919—January 6, 1923. *Also 1* telegram. September 20, 1919.

SHAPIRO (R.). *1.* Undated.

SHARP (Clifford Dyce). *1.* July 5, 1922.

SHAW-LEFEVRE (George John), *1st Baron Eversley of Old Ford, London. 9.* May 20, 1913—October 21, 1921.

SHELLY (John). *5.* December 1, 1907—November 18, 1911.

SHERRINGTON (*Sir* Charles Scott). *3.* December 30, 1921—January 20, 1926.

SHIPLEY (Marie Adelaide), *née* Brown [Mrs. John B. Shipley], *see* BROWN (Marie Adelaide), *afterwards* Mrs. John B. Shipley.

SHORT (Wilfrid Maurice). *1.* August 8, 1918.

—— [*for* Arthur James Balfour, *1st Earl of Balfour*]. *2.* October 24, 1908; 1 undated.

SHORTER (Clement King). *1.* December 22, 1914.

—— *from* GOSSE (*Sir* Edmund William). *95.* July 20, 1887—February 16, 1916; 4 undated.

SHORTHOUSE (Joseph Henry). *47.* April 1, 1883—March 5, 1902.

SHORTHOUSE (Sarah) [Mrs. Joseph Henry Shorthouse]. *1.*
September 9, 1902.
Unsigned.

SICKERT (Walter Richard). *2.* January 2, 1924; 1 undated.

SIDGWICK (Henry). *7.* April 30, [1893]—June 30, 1900;
1 undated.

—— *to* STEPHEN (*Sir* Leslie). *1.* January 18, 1898.
Enclosed in a letter from Sir Leslie Stephen to Sir Edmund Gosse, dated
January 19, 1898.

SIM (*Sir* William Alexander). *2.* August 14, [1920?];
November 24, 1926.

SIMCOX (George Augustus). *2.* December 16, [1873]; 1
undated.

SIMON (John Allsebrook), *1st Viscount Simon of Stackpole Elidor.*
2. May 15, 1914; June 23, 1914.

—— *to* ASQUITH (Herbert Henry), *1st Earl of Oxford and
Asquith.* *1.* December 3, 1914.
Enclosed in a letter from the Earl of Oxford to Sir Edmund Gosse, dated
December 4, 1914.

SIMPSON (Evelyn Mary) [Mrs. Percy Simpson]. *1.* February
20, 1925.

SINCLAIR (John), *1st Baron Pentland of Lyth.* *1.* June 17, 1924.

SINGH (*Sir* Bhawani), *Bahadur, Maharaj Rana of Jhalawar.* *1.*
December 13, 1912.

SITWELL (Edith). *2.* May 9, 1923; June 14, 1923.

SITWELL (*Sir* Osbert), *5th Bart.* *1.* January 10, 1925.

SKEAT (Walter William). *1.* January 4, 1885.

SKIPIS (Sotiris). *1.* December 15, 1926.

SKIPSEY (Joseph). *2.* May 16, 1889; May 18, 1889.

SLÁDEK (Josef V.). *2.* May 17, 1892; December 6, 1892.

SMITH (A.) *to* WISE (Thomas James). *1.* July 30, [1915].

SMITH (A. Fowler). *1.* February 21, 1884.

SMITH (Frederick Edwin), *1st Earl of Birkenhead.* *1.* January
20, 1926.

SMITH (George Charles Moore). *1.* September 11, 1926.

SMITH (George Gregory). *1.* November 6, 1892.

SMITH (Helen F.). *1.* March 5, 1885.

SMITH (John Alexander) *to* ROSS (A. G.). *1.* January 10,
1919.

SMITH (Logan Pearsall) *to* ROSS (A. G.). *1.* May 13, 1919.

SMITH (Roswell) *from* MUNRO (David A.). *1.* May 24, 1889.
Typewritten copy. Enclosed in a letter [June? 1889] from Viscount
Wolseley to Sir Edmund Gosse.

SMITH (William Robertson). *8.* July 21, 1884—November 28, 1892; 1 undated.
The letter dated November 28, 1892, is a copy, in the handwriting of Sir Edmund Gosse.

SMYTH (*Dame* Ethel Mary). *1.* November 16, 1900.

SNOILSKY (Carl Johan Gustaf), *pseud.* Sven Tröst. *1.* November 2, 1873.

SOMERSET (*Lady* Isabella Caroline). *1.* April 15, [1920].

SOUTHBOROUGH (Francis John Stephens Hopwood, *1st Baron*), *see* HOPWOOD (Francis John Stephens), *1st Baron Southborough of Southborough.*

SPENCE (M. M.). *1.* February 12, 1884.

SPENCER (*Lady* Adelaide Margaret Delia), *afterwards* Peel. *3.* April 15, 1911—October 6, 1922.

SPENCER (*Lady* Alexandra Margaret Elizabeth), *afterwards* Douglas-Home. *2.* August 4, 1922; August 12, [1925].

SPENCER (Charles Robert), *6th Earl Spencer. 211.* May 26, 1908—July 31, 1922. *Also 1* telegram. August 13, 1910.

—— *to* GOSSE (Ellen, *Lady*). *1.* March 3, 1922.

—— *to* Ross (A. G.). *1.* December 18, 1918.

SPENCER (*Lady* Lavinia Emily), *afterwards* Baroness Annaly. *1.* April 18, 1913.

SPIELMANN (Marion Harry Alexander). *1.* September 27, 1919.

SPOELBERCH DE LOVENJOUL (Alfred Charles Joseph de), *Vicomte. 1.* July 26, 1894.

SQUIRE (*Sir* John Collings). *37.* May 27, 1918—November 12, 1924; 1 undated.

STANHOPE (Edwyn Francis Scudamore-), *10th Earl of Chesterfield. 2.* April 22, 1910; May 5, 1910.

STANHOPE (Philip James), *1st Baron Weardale of Stanhope. 3.* December 14, 1908—October 10, 1913.

STANLEY (Edward Henry), *15th Earl of Derby, see* JUST (H. W.) [*for* Edward Henry Stanley, *15th Earl of Derby*].

STANLEY (*Lady* Maureen Helen), *née* Vane-Tempest-Stewart, *see* VANE-TEMPEST-STUART (*Lady* Maureen Helen), *afterwards* Stanley.

STANLEY (Oliver Frederick George). *1.* Undated.

STANMORE (Arthur Hamilton-Gordon, *1st Baron*), *see* GORDON (Arthur Hamilton-), *1st Baron Stanmore of Great Stanmore.*

STANMORE (George Arthur Maurice Hamilton-Gordon, *2nd Baron*), *see* GORDON (George Arthur Maurice Hamilton-), *2nd Baron Stanmore of Great Stanmore.*

STANTON (Vincent Henry). *1.* October 22, 1886.

STEAD (William Thomas). *5.* November 21, 1907— December 11, 1907.

STEDMAN (Edmund Clarence). *15.* November 29, 1875— January 13, 1886. *Also* a fragment of a letter, or post-script, undated and unsigned.

STEDMAN (Laura). *1.* December 7, 1908.

STEPHEN (*Sir* Herbert), *2nd Bart. 3.* February 9, 1904— August 7, 1923.

—— *to* GOSSE (Ellen, *Lady*). *1.* May 18, 1928.

—— *to* ROSS (A. G.). *1.* December 18, 1918.

STEPHEN (*Sir* Leslie). *46.* [1876]—June 29, 1902; 1 undated.

> Letter dated January 19, 1898: enclosed is a letter from Henry Sidgwick to Sir Leslie Stephen, dated January 18, 1898.
> Letter dated February 16, 1898: attached is a copy, in Sir Edmund Gosse's hand, of the original enclosure—a letter from Meredith to Sir Leslie Stephen, dated February 14, 1898.

—— *from* MEREDITH (George). *1.* February 14, 1898.

> A copy, in Sir Edmund Gosse's hand, attached to a letter dated February 16, 1898, from Sir Leslie Stephen to Sir Edmund Gosse, enclosing the original, which was returned.

—— *from* SIDGWICK (Henry). *1.* January 18, 1898.

> Enclosed in a letter from Sir Leslie Stephen to Sir Edmund Gosse, dated January 19, 1898.

STEVENSON (Harriette Louisa) [Mrs. Robert Alan Mowbray Stevenson]. *5.* May 1, [1908]—January 8, [1909].

STEVENSON (Margaret M.). *4.* [February, 1909?]—[March 29? 1909].

STEWART (Hugh Fraser). *1.* September 23, 1919.

STOCKTON (Francis Richard). *8.* May 7, 1884—July 21, 1895.

—— *see also* HALE (Edward Everett) *to* STOCKTON [Francis Richard Stockton?].

STODDARD (Richard Henry). *4.* January 4, 1885—January 21, 1885; 1 undated.

STOKES (Henry Sewell). *2.* April 11, 1876; April 23, 1876.

STORRS (*Sir* Ronald). *1.* January 17, 1927.

STRACHEY (Giles Lytton). *9.* April 18, 1922—April 27, 1926.

STRACHEY (John St. Loe). *3.* December 30, 1921—August 13, 1925.

> Letter of August 13, 1925, signed 'J. St. Loe Strachey per N.E.'

STREET (George Slythe). *7.* January 21, 1901—March 14, 1920.
—— *to* GOSSE (Philip). *1.* August 28, 1931.
STRODTMANN (Adolf). *1.* (February 11, 1879).
STRONG (Isobel Stuart), *née* Osbourne [Mrs. Joseph Dwight Strong]. *2.* [March 8, 1899]; [November 25, 1901].
STRUTT (Robert John), *4th Baron Rayleigh of Terling Place. 1.* October 8, 1926.
STURGIS (Julian) *to* BENSON (Arthur Christopher). *1.* February 13, [1902].
   Enclosed in a letter from A. C. Benson to Sir Edmund Gosse, dated February 14, 1902. Incomplete. The signature is added in Sir Edmund Gosse's hand.
STURGIS (*Sir* Mark Beresford Russell Grant-). *1.* September 13, 1909.
SUMMERS (Alphonsus Joseph-Mary Augustus Montague). *2.* September 20, 1919; August 12, 1925.
SUNDAY TIMES *from* BEERBOHM (*Sir* Max). *1.* [May 18, 1928].
—— *see also* GARDNER (Thomas A.) [*for* the *Sunday Times*].
SVANBERG (Harald). *1.* June 20, 1909.
SWANWICK (Anna). *1.* February 7, [1884?].
SWETTENHAM (*Sir* Frank Athelstane). *2.* February 1, [1901]; 1 undated.
SWIFT (Benjamin) *pseud.* [*i.e.* William Romaine Paterson], *see* PATERSON (William Romaine), *pseud.* Benjamin Swift.
SWINBURNE (Algernon Charles). *86.* September 14, 1867—April 7, 1907.
   Twenty-five letters, written during the period October 30, [1874]—January 12, 1898, are holograph. The rest are typewritten transcripts.
—— *to* GOSSE (Ellen, *Lady*). *4.* January 10, [1877]—July 29, 1882.
—— *from* BRADLEY (Kathleen Harris) *and* COOPER (Edith Emma), *pseud.* Michael Field. *1.* [June 19, 1895].
—— *from* GOSSE (*Sir* Edmund William). *2.* November 19, 1880; March 2, 1881.
SWINBURNE (Isabel) *to* WISE (Thomas James). *2.* May 22, 1915; May 24, 1915.
   Returned enclosed in letters from Sir Edmund Gosse to T. J. Wise dated May 25, 1915, and May 26, 1915.
SYDENHAM OF COMBE (George Sydenham Clarke, *1st Baron*), *see* CLARKE (George Sydenham), *1st Baron Sydenham of Combe.*
SYMONDS (John Addington). *67.* August 7, 1875—January 10, 1893.

SYMONS (Arthur). *60.* May 11, 1890—May 23, 1908.
—— *to* GOSSE (Ellen, *Lady*). *1.* Undated.
SYMONS (Rhoda) [Mrs. Arthur Symons] *to* BALFOUR (Arthur James), *1st Earl of Balfour. 1.* October 22, [1908].
SYSONBY (Frederick Edward Grey Ponsonby, *1st Baron*), *see* PONSONBY (Frederick Edward Grey), *1st Baron Sysonby of Wonersh.*
SZILY VON NAGYSZIGETH (Coloman) [*for* the Hungarian Academy of Sciences]. *1.* February 2, 1897.
Signed: 'Le secrétaire général C. de Szily.'

T

TADEMA (Anna Alma-). *1.* September 20, 1919.
TADEMA (Laura Theresa, *Lady* Alma-) *to* GOSSE (*Sir* Edmund William) *and* GOSSE (Ellen, *Lady*). *1.* [April 9? 1878].
Written in the blank space beneath the postscript of a letter from Sir Lawrence Alma-Tadema to Sir Edmund and Lady Gosse, dated April 8—9, 1878.
TADEMA (Laurence Alma-). *6.* October 25, 1908— September 21, 1919.
TADEMA (*Sir* Lawrence Alma-). *11.* March 11, 1876— April 19, 1904. *Also* a fragment of a letter, undated and unsigned.
—— *to* GOSSE (*Sir* Edmund William) *and* GOSSE (Ellen, *Lady*). *4.* August 25, 1875—August 17, 1900.
Letter of April 8—9, 1878: written in the blank space beneath the postscript is a note from Lady Alma-Tadema to Sir Edmund and Lady Gosse.
—— *to* GOSSE (Ellen, *Lady*). *1.* December 5, 1874.
TAFT (William Howard). *2.* September 4, 1914; October 26, 1914.
TARDIVEAU (René Marie Auguste), *pseud.* René Boylesve. *3.* September 22, 1903—August 5, 1921.
TAYLOR INSTITUTION, *see* WRIGHT (Joseph) [*for* the Curators of the Taylor Institution].
TAYLOR (*Sir* Henry). *1.* July 6, 1884.
TAYLOR (Rachel Annand). *1.* October 11, 1912.
TENNYSON (Hallam), *2nd Baron Tennyson of Aldworth and Farringford. 2.* November, 1883; December 3, 1914.
THACKERAY (Anne Isabella), *afterwards* Lady Ritchie. *11.* [April 23, 1895]—November 27, 1915; 1 undated.
THOMAS (Edith Matilda). *1.* January 16, 1906.
THOMMESSEN (Olaus Anton). *2.* August 29, 1901; March 2, 1902.

THOMPSON (*Sir* Edward Maunde). *1.* February 9, 1904.

THOMPSON (Rupert). *1.* July 25, 1927.

THOMPSON (William Hepworth). *12.* March 30, 1883—
June 12, 1886.

——*from* COLVIN (*Sir* Sidney). *1.* April 22, 1883.

THOMSEN (Vilhelm Ludvig Peter). *4.* January 26, 1875—
December 5, 1878.

THORNYCROFT (Agatha, *Lady*). *2.* December 12, [1925];
December 16, 1925.

—— *to* SASSOON (Siegfried Lorraine). *1.* June 8, [1927?].

THORNYCROFT (*Sir* William Hamo). *71.* July 15, 1879—
December 11, 1925; 1 undated. *Also* a detached postscript, undated.

Letter dated [*c.* November 25, 1916]: enclosed is a letter from Lord
Harcourt to Sir Edmund Gosse, dated November 23, 1916.

—— *to* GOSSE (*Sir* Edmund William) *and* GOSSE (Ellen, *Lady*).
1 telegram. August 12, 1925.

—— *to* WALDEGRAVE (William Frederick), *9th Earl Waldegrave.* *1.* June 3, 1907.

THORPE (Nelly) [Mrs. Roby Thorpe] *to* ROSS (A. G.). *1.*
January 13, 1919.

THURSFIELD (*Sir* James Richard). *1.* September 22, 1919.

THYNNE (Thomas Henry), *5th Marquis of Bath.* *1.* July 26,
1921.

TINSON (Harold). *1.* December 23, 1905.

TINWORTH (George). *6.* April 22, 1882—January 21, 1892;
2 undated.

TOBIN (Agnes). *1.* September 13, 1907.

TOPELIUS (Zacharias). *1.* August 7, 1876.

TORELLI-VIOLLIER (Maria) [Mme. Eugenio Torelli-
Viollier], *pseud.* Marchesa Colombi. *1.* November 26,
1883.

TOURGUÉNEFF (Ivan Sergyeevitch). *1.* December 27, 1881.

TOWNESEND (Frances Eliza Hodgson) [Mrs. Stephen Towne-
send], *formerly* Mrs. Swan Moses Burnett, *see* BURNETT
(Frances Eliza Hodgson) [Mrs. Swan Moses Burnett],
afterwards Mrs. Stephen Townesend.

TOYNBEE (Paget). *2.* June 28, 1927; July 4, 1927.

TRAILL (Henry Duff). *4.* October 22, 1886—February 14,
1898.

TREE (*Sir* Herbert Beerbohm). *3.* September 22, 1902—
January 19, 1915

TREFUSIS (*Lady* Mary) [*for* Mary, *Queen Consort of King George V*]. *3*. March 12, 1909—March 19, 1909.

TRENCH (Herbert). *1*. November 22, 1911.

TRENCH (Richard Chenevix), *Archbishop of Dublin*. *1*. January 10, 1884.
Unsigned.

TREVELYAN (George Macaulay). *2*. May 6, 1910; October 11, 1919.

TREVELYAN (*Sir* George Otto), *2nd Bart*. *21*. February 11, 1897—July 21, 1925.

TREVES (*Sir* Frederick), *1st Bart*. *9*. December 30, 1917—August 16, 1923.

TROELS-LUND (Troels Frederik), *see* LUND (Troels Frederik).

TRÖST (Sven) *pseud*. [*i.e.* Carl Johan Gustaf Snoilsky], *see* SNOILSKY (Carl Johan Gustaf), *pseud*. Sven Tröst.

TURGENEV (Ivan Sergyeevitch), *see* TOURGUÉNEFF (Ivan Sergyeevitch).

TURNER (L. Godfrey) *to* BROTHERTON (Edward Allen), *1st Baron Brotherton of Wakefield*. *1*. July 2, 1929.
Enclosed: a letter from Sir Edmund Gosse to L. G. Turner, dated January 26, 1928.

——*from* GOSSE (*Sir* Edmund William). *1*. January 26, 1928.
Enclosed in a letter from L. G. Turner to Lord Brotherton, dated July 2, 1929.

TURNER (Robert S.). *2*. January 16, 1884; February 6, 1884.

TWEEDMOUTH (Edward Marjoribanks, *2nd Baron*), *see* MARJORIBANKS (Edward), *2nd Baron Tweedmouth of Edington*.

TWEEDSMUIR (John Buchan, *1st Baron*), *see* BUCHAN (John), *1st Baron Tweedsmuir of Elsfield*.

TYRRELL (Robert Yelverton). *1*. February 15, [1894?].

U

ULLSWATER (James William Lowther, *1st Viscount*), *see* LOWTHER (James William), *1st Viscount Ullswater of Campsea Ashe*.

V

VALDÉS (Armando Palacio), *see* PALACIO VALDÉS (Armando).

VALLENTIN (Hugo). *1*. September 21, 1919.

VAN DER POEL (A.) *to* GOSSE (Philip). *1*. April 20, 1936.

VANE-TEMPEST-STEWART (Charles Stewart), *6th Marquis of Londonderry.* 7. April 27, 1889—May 8, 1912; 2 undated.

VANE-TEMPEST-STEWART (Charles Stewart Henry), *7th Marquis of Londonderry.* 10. May 17, 1906—January 28, 1921; 2 undated.

—— *to* ROSS (A. G.). 1. December 17, 1918.

VANE-TEMPEST-STEWART (Edith Helen), *Marchioness of Londonderry.* 5. April 7, [1907]—June 12, [1923]; 2 undated.

VANE-TEMPEST-STEWART (*Lady* Maureen Helen), *afterwards* Stanley. 1. June 25, [1920].

VANE-TEMPEST-STEWART (Theresa Susey Helen), *Marchioness of Londonderry.* 14. January, [1899]—[March 11, 1919].

—— *to* ROSS (A. G.). 1. December 28, 1918.

—— *from* GOSSE (*Sir* Edmund William). 1. February 9, 1914.
A copy, in Sir Edmund Gosse's hand.

VANSITTART (Robert Gilbert), *1st Baron Vansittart of Denham.* 1. October 8, 1910.

VENABLES (Edmund). 1. January 22, 1884.

VERHAEREN (Émile). 6. (February 21, 1902)—(February 2, 1915).

VERNEY (Richard Greville), *19th Baron Willoughby de Broke.* 6. April 1, 1913—June 11, 1921.

VERRALL (Arthur Woollgar). *12.* April 14, 1885—February 25, 1912.
The letter dated February 25, 1912, is in another hand, and is signed "A. W. Verrall (per H. de G. V.)."

VIELÉ-GRIFFIN (Francis). 5. September 10, 1896—September 3, 1925. *Also* 1 telegram. September 22, 1916.

VIGFÚSSON (Guðbrandur). 1. July 17, 1875.

VILLARS (Paul). 6. February 26, 1898—October 23, 1913.

VILLIERS (Edward Hyde), *5th Earl of Clarendon.* 1. February 16, 1912.

VILLIERS (Margaret Elizabeth Child-), *Countess of Jersey.* 1. September 19, 1925.

VINES (Sydney Howard). 9. February 17, 1907—November 8, 1920.

VOGT (Nils Collett). 1. October 24, 1899.

VOGT (Paul Benjamin). 1. September 22, 1919.

VONTADE (Jacques) *pseud.* [*i.e.* Mme. A. Bulteau], *see* BULTEAU (*Mme.* A.), *pseuds.* Jacques Vontade; Fœmina.

VOSMAER (Carel). *8.* October 1, 1877—March 15, 1879; 1 undated.

W

WAGSTAFF (W. H.) [*for* the Royal Society of Literature of the United Kingdom] *to* GOSSE (Ellen, *Lady*). *1.* May 23, 1928.

WALDEGRAVE (William Frederick), *9th Earl Waldegrave, from* THORNYCROFT (*Sir* William Hamo). *1.* June 3, 1907.

WALISZEWSKI (Casimir). *1.* January 20, 1899.

WALLACE (Alfred Russel). *3.* February 16, 1886—February 17, 1898.

WALLIS (Henry). *3.* February 12, [1884?]—May 25, [1885].

WALLOP (Newton), *6th Earl of Portsmouth.* *2.* March 9, 1908; April 19, 1910.

WALPOLE (Robert Horace), *5th Earl of Orford.* *1.* December 23, 1913.

WALPOLE (Spencer Horatio). *2.* December 6, 1883; [*c.* February, 1884].

WALSINGHAM (Thomas de Grey, *6th Baron*), *see* DE GREY (Thomas), *6th Baron Walsingham of Walsingham.*

WARD (Mary Augusta) [Mrs. Humphry Ward]. *11.* November 11, 1890—May 17, 1905.

WARD (T. M.). *1.* July 19, 1905.

WARD (Thomas Humphry). *5.* December 20, [1883?]— November 5, 1914.

—— *from* BALFOUR (Arthur James), *1st Earl of Balfour.* *1.* February 10, 1893.

WARREN (John Byrne Leicester), *3rd Baron de Tabley.* *178.* March 23, 1876—September 17, 1895; 21 undated.

WARREN (*Sir* Thomas Herbert). *5.* June 14, 1912— December 19, 1927.

—— *to* ROSS (A. G.). *1.* December 18, 1918.

WATERHOUSE (Alfred). *6.* January 20, 1881—July 3, 1893.

WATERHOUSE (Paul). *1.* April 21, 1907.

WATSON (Henry Brereton Marriott). *6.* January 7, 1899— October 15, 1914.

—— *from* SEAMAN (*Sir* Owen), *1st Bart.* *1.* October 8, 1914.

WATSON (Robinson). *7.* February 6, 1893—March 29, 1893. *Also 1* telegram. February 13, 1893.

—— *to* GOSSE (Ellen, *Lady*). *2.* March 14, 1893; March 24, [1893].

—— *from* GOSSE (*Sir* Edmund William). *1.* March 10, 1893.

WATSON (*Sir* William). *19.* December 10, (1891)—June 7, 1917; 2 undated.

—— *from* GOSSE (*Sir* Edmund William). *14.* June 21, 1880—December 15, 1916.

All except one, dated February 27, 1882, are typewritten transcripts.

WATTS (George Frederic). *10.* January 1, 1882—December 4, 1898.

WATTS (Walter Theodore), *afterwards* Watts-Dunton. *26.* September 29, 1879—July 26, 1903; 1 undated. *Also 1* telegram. July 21, 1899.

—— *to* GOSSE (*Sir* Edmund William) *and* SCHWARTZ (Joost Marius Willem van der Poorten-), *pseud.* Maarten Maartens. *1.* June 10, 1895.

—— *to* WISE (Thomas James). *6.* June 28, 1909—April 26, 1914; 1 undated.

Wise sent four of the letters, upon receipt, to Sir Edmund Gosse, attaching in each case a covering note.

—— *from* GOSSE (*Sir* Edmund William). *27.* May 4, 1876—May 31, 1902; 5 undated.

The letter dated October 2, 1879, is a typewritten copy.

WAUGH (Arthur). *7.* [April 17, 1894]—September 20, 1919.

—— *to* ROSS (A. G.). *1.* May 11, 1919.

—— [*for* Chapman & Hall Ltd., *publishers*]. *5.* February 4, 1927—May 9, 1927.

WAY (W. Irving). *2.* November 1, 1883; September 18, 1884.

WAYTE (William). *1.* October 29, 1884.

WEARDALE (Philip James Stanhope, *1st Baron*), *see* STANHOPE (Philip James), *1st Baron Weardale of Stanhope*.

WEBB (*Sir* Aston). *1.* December 10, 1919.

WEBSTER (Julia Augusta) [Mrs. Thomas Webster], *pseud.* Cecil Home. *6.* January 12, 1874—April 17, [1879].

WEBSTER (Richard Everard), *1st Viscount Alverstone of Alverstone*. *1.* February 11, 1908.

—— *from* BALFOUR (Arthur James), *1st Earl of Balfour*. *1.* October 6, 1896.

—— *from* BENSON (Edward White), *Archbishop of Canterbury*. *1.* September 15, 1896.

Transcript only.

WEDMORE (*Sir* Frederick). *2.* January 3, 1912; October 21, 1913.
—— *to* KELLY (James Fitzmaurice-). *1.* November 11, [1920].
Written on his behalf in an unidentified hand.
WELLS (Amy Catherine) [Mrs. Herbert George Wells]. *2.* [1904?]; 1 undated.
WELLS (Herbert George). *24.* October 2, 1897—[October 2, 1912]; 2 undated.
—— *to* Ross (A. G.). *1.* [May? 1919].
—— *from* GISSING (Algernon). *1.* May 28, 1912.
WEMYSS-CHARTERIS-DOUGLAS (Francis Richard), *10th Earl of Wemyss. 2.* April 18, 1910; [April 5, 1913]. *Also 1* telegram. August 4, 1913.
WEMYSS-CHARTERIS-DOUGLAS (Grace), *Countess of Wemyss. 1.* [December, 1913?].
WENTWORTH (Judith Anne Dorothea Milbanke, *Baroness*), *see* LYTTON (Judith Anne Dorothea Blunt-), *afterwards* Milbanke, *Baroness Wentworth.*
WEST (Beatrice Stella Cornwallis-) [Mrs. George Frederick Myddleton Cornwallis-West], *formerly* Mrs. Patrick Campbell, *see* CAMPBELL (Beatrice Stella) [Mrs. Patrick Campbell], *afterwards* Mrs. George Frederick Myddleton Cornwallis-West.
WEST (Josephine Victoria Sackville-), *Baroness Sackville. 1.* August 13, 1925.
WEST (Lionel Edward Sackville-), *3rd Baron Sackville of Knole. 1.* November 19, 1911.
WESTBURY (Florence). *1.* May 15, [1895].
WESTMINSTER (Hugh Lupus Grosvenor, *1st Duke of*), *see* SCOTLAND (D.) [*for* Hugh Lupus Grosvenor, *1st Duke of Westminster*].
WHARTON (Edith Newbold) [Mrs. Edward Wharton]. *12.* February 18, 1911—January 3, 1925; 2 undated.
—— *to* LAPSLEY (Gaillard Thomas). *1.* February 7, 1911.
WHIBLEY (Charles). *11.* February 4, [1916]—January 4, [1919]; 5 undated.
WHITE (Lavinia Emily), *Baroness Annaly, née* Spencer, *see* SPENCER (*Lady* Lavinia Emily), *afterwards* Baroness Annaly.
WHITE (Luke Henry), *4th Baron Annaly of Annaly and Rathcline. 1.* August 14, 1925.

WHITTINGHAM (Charles) & Co., *printers*. *1*. November 13, 1913.

WIGGIN (Kate Douglas) [Mrs. Samuel Bradley Wiggin], *afterwards* Mrs. George Christopher Riggs. *2*. [May 21, 1909]; September 22, 1919.

WILLOUGHBY DE BROKE (Richard Greville Verney, *19th Baron*), *see* VERNEY (Richard Greville), *19th Baron Willoughby de Broke*.

WILSON (*Sir* Guy Douglas Arthur Fleetwood). *2*. July 15, [1922]; August 13, 1925.

WILSON (*Sir* Henry Francis). *1*. October 3, 1919.

WINTER-HJELM (Kristian Anastas). *1*. December 1, 1872.

WINTHER (Rasmus Villads Christian Ferdinand). *2*. July 9, 1874; July 29, 1874.

WIRGMAN (Theodore Blake). *1*. September 23, 1919.

WIRSÉN (Carl David af). *4*. January 28, 1879—May 16, 1888.

WISE (Thomas James). *128*. March 9, 1908—January 1, 1928; 1 undated.

Letter of June 29, 1909: enclosed is a letter from W. T. Watts-Dunton to T. J. Wise, dated the previous day.

Letter of September 17, 1909: written on the back of a letter from A. W. Pollard to T. J. Wise, dated [September 16? 1909].

Letter dated [November 30? 1909]: written in the space below the signature of a letter from W. T. Watts-Dunton to Wise, dated November 29, 1909.

Letters of February 5 and April 27, 1914: enclosed are letters from W. T. Watts-Dunton to T. J. Wise, dated in each case the previous day.

Letter of November 26, 1917: enclosed is a letter from W. W. Caddell to Sir Edmund Gosse, dated November 25, 1917; also rough draft of reply suggested by Wise.

—— *from* GOSSE (*Sir* Edmund William). *398*. June 21, 1893—February 25, 1928; 2 undated.

Also part of a letter in Sir Edmund Gosse's hand, signed, with post-script—presumably to Wise; undated.

Letters of May 25 and 26, 1915: enclosed are two letters from Isabel Swinburne to T. J. Wise, dated May 22 and May 24.

—— *from* LEITH (Mary Charlotte Julia) [Mrs. Disney Leith]. *1*. August 3, 1915.

—— *from* LEMPERLY (Paul). *1*. July 4, 1909.

—— *from* POLLARD (Alfred William). *2*. [September 16? 1909]; January 7, 1913.

Letter dated [September 16? 1909]: written on the back is a letter from T. J. Wise to Sir Edmund Gosse, dated September 17, 1909.

—— *from* SMITH (A.). *1*. July 30, [1915].

——*from* SWINBURNE (Isabel). *2.* May 22, 1915; May 24, 1915.
Returned enclosed in letters from Sir Edmund Gosse to T. J. Wise dated May 25, 1915, and May 26, 1915.

——*from* WATTS (Walter Theodore), *afterwards* Watts-Dunton. *6.* June 28, 1909—April 26, 1914; 1 undated.
Wise sent four of the letters, upon receipt, to Sir Edmund Gosse, attaching in each case a covering note.

WISTER (Owen). *2.* October 28, 1915; April 22, 1923.

WITHERS (Percy). *1.* November 15, 1920.

WOLFE (Humbert) *to* BATEMAN (*Sir* Alfred Edmund). *1.* May 7, 1928.

WOLFF METTERNICH ZUR GRACHT (Paul Wolff Metternich, *Graf*), *see* METTERNICH (Paul Wolff), *Graf Wolff Metternich zur Gracht.*

WOLSELEY (Frances Garnet), *Viscountess Wolseley. 2.* October 15, 1925; November 3, 1925.

WOLSELEY (Garnet Joseph), *1st Viscount Wolseley. 25.* [April 7, 1889]—August 5, 1905.
Letter dated [June? 1889]: enclosed is a typewritten copy of a letter from David A. Munro to Roswell Smith, President of the Century Company, New York, dated May 24, 1889.

—— *to* GOSSE (Ellen, *Lady*). *1* telegram. September 19, 1899.

——*from* GOSSE (*Sir* Edmund William). *1.* June 30, 1889.

WOLSELEY (Louisa), *Viscountess Wolseley. 12.* [December 18, 1888]—April 22, 1908.

—— *to* GOSSE (Ellen, *Lady*). *1.* June 5, 1892.

—— *see also* DOWDEN (Edward) *to* WOLSELEY, *Lady* [Louisa, Viscountess Wolseley ?].

WOOD (Charles Lindley), *2nd Viscount Halifax. 14.* February 24, 1907—January 3, 1921; 1 undated.

WOOD (Edward Frederick Lindley), *1st Earl of Halifax. 2.* January 1, 1926; January 4, 1926.

WOODBERRY (George Edward). *1.* November 13, 1909.

WOODFORD (James Russell), *Bishop of Ely. 1.* March 5, [1885].

WOOLNER (Thomas). *11.* May 30, 1881—June 3, 1883; 1 undated.
Letter dated [February? 1882]: enclosed is a letter from Julius Haehnel to Thomas Woolner, dated January 5, 1882.

——*from* HAEHNEL (Julius). *2.* December 20, 1881; January 5, 1882.
Letter of January 5, 1882: enclosed in a letter from Thomas Woolner to Sir Edmund Gosse, dated [February? 1882].

WRATISLAW (Theodore) *to* GOSSE (*Sir* Edmund William) *and* GOSSE (Ellen, *Lady*). *1.* August 11, 1925.

WRIGHT (*Sir* Charles Theodore Hagberg). *1.* August 12, 1925.

WRIGHT (Joseph) [*for* the Curators of the Taylor Institution]. *1.* February 7, 1925.

WRIGHT (William Aldis). *32.* July 9, 1882—February 8, 1907.

——*from* FURNIVALL (Frederick James). *1.* February 28, 1905.

WYNDHAM (Charles Henry), *3rd Baron Leconfield of Leconfield*. *1.* December 3, 1901.

—— *to* LYTTON (Victor Alexander George Robert Bulwer-), *2nd Earl of Lytton*. *1.* November 19, 1901.

WYNDHAM (Constance Evelyn), *Baroness Leconfield*, *to* GARDNER (Winifred Anne Henrietta Christina), *Baroness Burghclere*. *1.* December 20, [1913].
Enclosed in a letter from Lady Burghclere to Sir Edmund Gosse, dated 'Xmas Day, 1913.'

WYNDHAM (George). *3.* January 3, 1890—July 27, 1910.

WYSEUR (Marcel). *2.* Undated.

WYZEWA (Teodor de). *1.* [August 13, 1895].

Υ

YEATS (William Butler). *25.* [July 23, 1903]—February 28, [1917].

YOUNG (Stark). *1.* [July 23, 1913].

YOUNGHUSBAND (*Sir* Francis Edward). *1.* June 15, 1924.

YŪSUF 'ALĪ ('Abd Allāh). *1.* September 22, 1919.

Z

ZANGWILL (Israel). *2.* October 31, 1911; September 21, 1919.

PRINTED BY E. J. ARNOLD & SON LTD. LEEDS 10